D1230062

+ 3ʳᵈ

15 Illos,

Wings.

CHARLES ROGERS AS JOHN POWELL AND
CLARA BOW AS CLARA PRESTON.

WINGS

BY

JOHN MONK SAUNDERS

BASED ON THE PARAMOUNT PICTURE

A LUCIEN HUBBARD PRODUCTION

DIRECTED BY WILLIAM A. WELLMAN

ILLUSTRATED WITH SCENES
FROM THE PHOTOPLAY

GROSSET & DUNLAP
PUBLISHERS   NEW YORK

PUBLISHED BY ARRANGEMENT WITH G. P. PUTNAM'S SONS

TO THOSE YOUNG WARRIORS OF THE SKY
WHOSE WINGS ARE FOLDED ABOUT THEM
FOREVER THIS BOOK AND THE MOTION
PICTURE ARE REVERENTLY DEDICATED.

CONTENTS

PART I

THE SHOOTING STAR

WINGS

PART I

THE SHOOTING STAR

JOHNNY POWELL was mowing the terrace when Dr. MacRoberts came down Mulberry Street in his new Ford runabout. Everyone in the neighborhood, practically, knew that the Doctor had bought himself a flivver. An unworldly little man of uncertain temper, he had long scorned motors and motorists and his capitulation to the new notion of progress had been as abrupt as unexpected.

He had insisted, after one impatient lesson at the wheel, that he was quite competent to operate the machine by himself, and Johnny Powell happened to be an eyewitness to the Doctor's maiden voyage in his new craft.

One thing the salesman had neglected to explain to the Doctor and that was that the front wheels of a flivver sometimes take to wabbling from side to side in an eccentric and unaccountable manner. "Shimmying," we called it then—this was in 1916 B.C. (Before the Charleston).

When therefore, in the middle of the block, the front wheels of the Doctor's car elected to flutter, like a trout's tail, the Doctor was disconcerted. Here was an emergency for which he was untutored. He pursued the only course he knew; he applied the foot brake and turned sharply in to the curb.

As a line of procedure under these circumstances, this was eminently correct. The only fault to be found with the Doctor's strategy was that, in his perturbation, he came down on the accelerator instead of the brake. The flivver, instantly inspired, hurdled the curb, tore through the shrubbery and climbed Johnny Powell's lawn. Halfway up the engine stalled and the car promptly started to slip backwards.

The Doctor emitted a despairing wail and

Johnny dropped the handle of his lawn-mower, leaped to the running board and gave the steering wheel a half-turn which brought the car to rest crosswise on the slope.

Dr. MacRoberts, whose dignity had been sadly jounced, descended with splendid hauteur, clapped his hat on his head, shot his cuffs, and stalked off in high dudgeon.

Johnny Powell ran after him. "I'll get it down for you, Doctor."

The Doctor did not check his stride nor turn his head.

"It's yours," he snapped with gesture of complete repudiation and continued his furious march to the trolley line.

Johnny fell back. A little dubious, he eased the abandoned flivver down across the sidewalk and onto the street. Then he went to work on the rhododendron bushes in the parking strip, cutting out the broken stalks and straightening the crushed branches. He approximated the fractured edges of a baby elm (his father would be distressed about that) and bound up the broken shaft

with bicycle tape. Then he trod out the
wheel marks in the soft turf on the terrace
and went inside to fetch his mother.

"See my new car," he said, pointing from
the porch.

His mother regarded the new flivver uncertainly.

"Whose is it?" she asked.

"Mine," said Johnny.

"How is it yours?"

"Doctor MacRoberts gave it to me."

"Why—how—" began his mother, puzzled.

Johnny told her what had happened.

"Ah, yes," said his mother understand-
ingly—she was not unacquainted with the
Doctor's caprices, "you must take it right
back to him."

"But he's gone down town."

"Well, leave it in front of his house then."

"But he said it was *mine*——"

"I know, son. But he didn't mean it—
really. Take it back."

Johnny took it back, with very bad grace.

But at four Mrs. MacRoberts called up

Johnny's house and told Johnny's mother
that Johnny was to come and take the car out
of the Doctor's sight. If he didn't want to
keep it, said Mrs. MacRoberts (to whom
the Doctor's tempers were not funny), he
was to take it down and run it into the lake.
The Doctor had probably damaged the Powell lawn more than the thing was worth and
besides the Doctor didn't want to be re-
minded of the accident—ever.

That was how Johnny Powell got his
flivver.

It can't be said that Johnny's parents
shared Johnny's elation over his windfall.
On the contrary, knowing Johnny's temper-
ament, they regarded the gift with grave
apprehension.

Johnny's father had persistently refused
to have a car in the family, at least while
Johnny was at the University, because he
believed that it would prove too great a
distraction for the boy. He would drive it
like the wind, he would be eternally tinker-
ing with it and would want to take it out at
night. It would be a constant temptation

to his son and a source of anxiety to his mother. So the elder Powell had gotten an electric brougham for Johnny's mother, a vehicle which Johnny resolutely disdained to be seen in.

Mrs. Powell derived some comfort from the fact that Johnny's new car was only a Ford. Fords didn't go *very* fast, did they? And you didn't hear of young boys and girls going on wild joy-rides in Fords? It was the high-powered cars. . . .

Could Johnny's mother have seen the bright vision in Johnny's blue eyes as he surveyed his gift-horse she would not have been so tranquil in her mind. For Johnny saw not the erect, black respectable Ford roadster, but a low-swung, stream-lined raceabout with a flaming yellow bonnet and a couple of bucket seats behind.

Boy! All you had to do was to strip 'er down, change the gearing, take off the mudguards and muffler and repaint the hood and wheels. Here was a job for Johnny's gifted hands.

Mary-Louise Preston was sitting on the

steps of her back porch with a peasant bowl between her knees, shelling peas, when Johnny ran the car up the driveway and into his back yard. An alley, a clean, white cement-paved alley (all alleys were like that in Temple, Washington—at least in the residential section) was all that separated the back yards of the Prestons and the Powells. The Powell residence faced east on Mulberry Street, whereas the Prestons' looked west upon Beech, so their respective back yards adjoined each other—that is except for the alley way which ran through the entire block.

Now there is a saying that there is no romance in a girl from your own home town. If that is true then there is still less romance in a girl whose back yard faces your own.

Johnny Powell had grown up with Mary-Louise Preston and he didn't know how pretty she was. Her fresh young skin, her evenly cut lips, and dark eyes would have bemused almost anybody; especially as she sat now, in a blue, short-sleeved print dress with a yellow bowl between her knees and the sun splintering against her blue-black hair.

Still you could hardly blame Johnny if he wasn't quickened to Mary's beauty. He saw her a dozen times a day on commonplace errands for her mother and there was little, if anything, about her that he did not know. Take her unmentionables, for instance, her pink slips and her step-ins and her panties. They were exposed to Johnny's eye every Tuesday when Amy, the colored laundress (she came to the Powells' on Mondays), flung them to the breezes on the Preston clothes-line.

Mary was no breathless mystery to Johnny, and it was a pity because Mary adored Johnny Powell.

"New car?" she called across in quick astonishment.

"Yep."

Mary put down her bowl and came over to see. She was a little hurt because she was invariably apprised of everything that transpired in Johnny's life and certainly he had told her nothing about this.

"Flivver?"

"Yep."

"Thought your father wouldn't let you have a car."

"He changed his mind." Johnny took up the seat, pulled out a kit of tools, unrolled them, selected a screw driver and a wrench and went to work on the right door hinge. Presently he lifted it off and stood it against the garage wall.

"Taking it apart?" Mary's voice was incredulous.

"That's right."

"What for?"

"Goin' to strip 'er down."

"Make a racer out of it!"

"Sure."

Mary clapped her hands. "Going to paint it too? Let me paint it for you, Johnny! Let *me*. Let me paint it!"

"All right," said Johnny, taking off the other door.

"What color, Johnny? Blue? Red? Yellow?"

"Yellow."

So it was agreed that when the car was ready, Mary should do the painting. She was very good at it, Johnny knew; she had painted much of the furniture in the Preston house and had decorated two of the upstairs rooms. Besides that she painted water colors and things.

Mary didn't go to the University. Not that her father couldn't send her. Temple was a university town and he might have managed all right. But Mary liked to paint and to practice on the piano and she could keep that up at home and anyway her mother wasn't always well and it was nice to have Mary at home.

Johnny Powell went to the University but his father, who was the Renaissance history professor there, wasn't at all sure that it was the right place for him. The truth of the matter was that Johnny wasn't faring any too well in his studies. In his required subjects especially, civics, economics, history and English literature. He was a good boy, his father told his mother, but he lacked a little of purpose.

His outstanding traits appeared to be his fondness for mechanics and his passion for speed. There wasn't a device in the Powell household that didn't work with smoothness and precision. If a stubborn window catch bruised his mother's thumb, Johnny, with an oil-can and a screw driver, had the thing working, click-click, in no time. There wasn't a door-hinge that squeaked, not a faulty light-connection, not a stiff lock mechanism in Johnny's house. They all yielded to Johnny's knowledgeable hands.

And what a pair of hands they were. Long straight flat-tipped fingers with well-kept nails. They were the hands of a surgeon, of a pianist or a thimble-rigger. There was knowledge in the finger tips, strength in the slim wrists. They were hands that could manage the wheel of a motor car—or, say, the controls of an airplane.

Johnny's bent for speed evidenced itself in many ways. He mowed the lawn with such a dash and clatter as to be practically enveloped in a cloud of grass ends as he raced from one side of the terrace to the other. When he was called upon to wax and polish the hardwood floors (as he was every Saturday morning) he zipped the weighted brush back and forth with such speed as to raise a blister on the surface of the oak.

As a boy, Johnny had the fastest roller coaster on the street, the swiftest sled on the hill, and nobody in the neighborhood could keep up with him on a bicycle. His father trembled to think what he would do with a motor car.

And now he had his car. To his father's consternation, his mother's dismay and to Mary's delight he went earnestly at the business of stripping down the Ford.

Now stripping down a flivver is not so simple as it sounds. True, the body comes off easily enough; there are only about eight bolts holding it down, and the fenders drop off when you loosen up a couple of nuts.

But when you get down to the chassis your troubles have only begun—if you really mean to have a raceabout. In the first place a flivver is too light and too high up in the air to hold the road when you get going. If

you want to go over fifty and still keep your
rear wheels from kicking off the ground
you've got to undersling. Set the front axle
ahead a few inches and suspend the engine
from the spring with a couple of wishbone
attachments. And you've got to get under-
slung parts. Johnny sent away for those.

You can't get much more than forty-five
miles an hour out of a Ford—except down-
hill. If you want more speed there are two
ways of getting it. One is to put in overhead valves and the other is to change the
gear ratio. Johnny Powell did both.

He wrote away for a new set of cylinder
heads and speed-gears. By opening up the
differential housing and slipping in the new
wheels he lowered the gear ratio from 3½-
1 to 3-1. The car wouldn't be so fast on the
pick-up, but, oh boy, on the straightaway!

Johnny wanted very badly to buy a racing body for the car but the new gears and
valves ate up all his spare money, so he had
to content himself with a wooden frame
which he bolted to the chassis.

The tinsmith across the bridge fashioned

a couple of bucket seats for him which he set up at an angle behind the wheel. From the car-wreckers behind Boyle's Garage he got, for $3.00, the gasoline tank "off an old Stutz" which he established on the shelf behind the seats. Besides looking very impressive back there, it held a lot of gas and helped to hold down the rear end of the car.

Over the Ford radiator the tinsmith also placed a pressed tin shell which fitted very snugly and concealed the lowly identity of the car. It was a Blitzen Benz or an Hispano-Suiza until you lifted up the hood and saw the little four-cylinder motor beneath.

While Johnny was engaged upon these mysterious operations Mary was busy with a can of acid and a scraper removing the black paint. The paint on a flivver is there to stay; if you paint over it, the original black will shine through sooner or later. You've got to get right down to the tin and paint up.

The two didn't get in each other's way much; Johnny was underneath a good part of the time and he didn't appear to be aware

of Mary's presence except when she dripped
paint in his eye or stepped on his neck.

The whole neighborhood was startled the
afternoon Johnny took the muffler off.

"Pretty?" inquired Johnny with a bea-
tific expression upon his countenance and
his ear cocked to the shattering stream of
explosions.

Mary, who had never before heard a Ford
engine with its muffler off, was a little astonished at its deep-voiced roar but she agreed
that it was lovely.

"Wait till I get her tuned up," Johnny
promised.

Those afternoons in the back yard were
joyful ones for Mary-Louise. She loved this
working association with Johnny and she
came to know a great deal about an automo-
bile. She could tell you (for Johnny explained to her) exactly what happened to a
drop of gasoline from the moment it entered
the tank until it was blown out the exhaust
pipe. She knew how it was vaporized, exploded, expelled.

She could tell the intake from the exhaust

valves, the oil from the water line. She knew
what a manifold was and a piston ring
and a clutch plate. She learned carburetion
and ignition and she could trace the cooling
and lubricating systems, knowledge that was
native to Johnny. And Johnny had promised to teach her to drive when the car was
ready.

Mary was secretly sorry when she saw
the great work coming to an end. It would
mean no more afternoons in the back yard
with Johnny but, she hoped, there would be
others out on the open road.

Mary thought there ought to be some kind
of christening ceremony the day they
launched the *Shooting Star*—at least Mary
called it the *Shooting Star* and she painted
one, a red one with a flaming yellow tail, on
the bonnet.

"Why the shooting star?" Johnny inquired.

"Well," Mary replied hesitantly, "it
looks like a shooting star and anyway have
you never heard the saying about a shooting star?"

"Nope. What is it?"

"Well," began Mary shyly, "well, the saying is . . . when you see a shooting star—
you can kiss the girl you love." She bent
her head down on the other side of the hood,
blushing furiously.

"Maybe I will," replied Johnny, a vision
of a blonde head and a pale upturned face
appearing before his eyes.

Poor Mary. The color died out of her
cheeks.

She didn't mention the christening ceremony to Johnny because he might laugh, and
it hurt Mary to have Johnny laugh at her
fancies. But she nursed her anticipation
for the great moment when the *Shooting
Star* would be ready and Johnny would tell
her to climb in and away they'd go. He
hadn't said anything about the exact time of
the maiden trip but Mary expected it would
be Saturday afternoon when the paint was
set. There it was now, crouching in
Johnny's back yard, all aflame with new
color, raring to go.

But Johnny Powell did not take Mary

for the maiden excursion in the *Shooting Star*.

On Friday afternoon she went to tea with Caroline Hotchkiss and on the way home she saw a canary colored roadster flash down Grove Street. It was the *Shooting Star*. Johnny was at the wheel and beside him a girl.

Mary halted, stricken with dismay. The first time out! The maiden trip! And he had taken someone else. Oh, Johnny, Johnny. Tears sprang to her eyes. Tears of disappointment, of humiliation, of hurt pride. Johnny had taken another girl for the first ride. She stumbled home and fled upstairs to her room.

Johnny had never said anything about the exact hour when he would take the car out or that he intended to take her out first. But you would naturally expect that he would take her, wouldn't you?

Mary had only just caught a glimpse of the girl but she knew it was Sylvia Lewis, the girl that everybody said Johnny was crazy about. Nobody knew why Sylvia had chosen to come to the quiet little western college when she might have gone anywhere to school. On account of her health, some-one said.

She lived in the east, Baltimore, or somewhere, and she came from a wealthy family. At least she dressed and talked as if she did. She had a clipped, aris-tocratic accent and a superior manner. She had a slender, drooping figure and a pale skin and gray eyes and a way of looking at you. And she was a blonde, an eye-widen-ing, breath-taking blonde.

During the college term she lived at the Kappa house, just across the street from the Sigma Chi's where Johnny belonged. Why did boys always fall for a girl like that?

When Johnny had gone to get Sylvia in the *Shooting Star,* he had found her dally-ing dreamily with Dave Armstrong on the Kappa porch-swing, whereupon, in his char-acteristic maner, he had seized her by the hand and torn her from his side. Further, and to insure Sylvia's person being properly cushioned upon the bare seat of the car, Johnny seized upon the ear of pillow peeping out from under Mr. David Armstrong, and gave it a healthy jerk, precipitating Mr. David Armstrong upon the floor.

From that vantage David observed Johnny Powell bestow Sylvia gallantly into his new car and whisk her away.

There was practically nothing in this entire procedure calculated to enhance John Powell's stature in the eyes of David Armstrong. But as he lifted himself off the floor and dusted off his white trousers he was able to smile at the impudence of the deed.

Armstrong was like that. He could smile because he felt the security of his own position with Sylvia. And anyway what Johnny had just done was the sort of feat that Armstrong himself could never bring himself to accomplish. The son of elderly, wealthy parents in Temple, he had been reared in an atmosphere of gentle manners and well-bred restraint. He lacked Johnny's mad impetuosity.

Johnny Powell, however, interpreted

David's natural reserve to a sense of superiority and a consciousness of money. Armstrong's appearance heightened this impression; he was tall, well-poised and had a certain grave assurance of manner.

Anyone, except perhaps Johnny Powell, could see that the tender Sylvia was more likely to respond to Armstrong's thoughtful nature than to Johnny's dash.

However, none could tell Johnny that, least of all, Mary. But it was the first of the heartbreaks for Mary. Still, her nature was utterly without vindictiveness, and when she heard Johnny hallooing in the back yard later in the afternoon she came down.

"Take a little ride?"

"I'd love to," she said brightly and she managed to smile when she climbed in.

The *Shooting Star* became famous in Temple and environs. Ladies with perambulators stopped and clucked their tongues; elderly gentlemen halted on street corners and wagged their heads, and small boys whooped when Johnny flashed past.

He even became the veiled subject of a

darkly prophetic editorial in the Temple
Vidette. An editorial directed at rich men's
sons and their high-powered motor-cars.
The fact that Johnny's father was not rich,
or that his car was a flivver, had nothing to
do with the conclusion that the younger gen-
eration was headed for trouble at a hell of
a clip. Johnny was viewed with alarm on
all sides.

He became "that boy with the yellow
racer."

He was the "speed merchant" of Temple
and was rumored to burn up the roads in
and about the quiet community. In short,
he became "Speed" Powell.

Rumors of these developments reached his
father but his father knew the "high-powered" car for a dressed-up flivver. Besides,
the car was Johnny's own; he had spent
many weeks and all of his pocket money on
it. As long as he had no accidents, broke no
laws and didn't keep it out unreasonably
late, the professor, a fair-minded man, saw
no occasion to interfere. He would have
preferred, all the same, that Johnny didn't

have the car, but since it was a *fait accompli* he did not protest. Certainly the *Shooting Star* hadn't improved Johnny's scholarship standing at the University.

Eight thousand miles away from the little college town where John Powell went his blonde-headed, blue-eyed way, two gentlemen were exchanging greetings.

The two gentlemen were three thousand meters in the air and bound in opposite directions. One was headed over the French lines for the purpose of making a military reconnaissance. The other was bent on a similar mission over the German lines. Passing, they saluted each other as befitted two officers engaged upon the most perilous pastime of the day: flying. *Morituri morituros salutant.*

But on the following day at the same hour, the one about to die did not salute the other about to die. Instead he drew his service revolver and took a pot-shot at the French pilot.

Up till this moment it had been generally agreed that flying was of itself a dangerous enough business without adding to its perils. To take up one of those early, treacherous, unstable craft and keep it in the air was considered precarious enough. The recoil of a gun, it was thought, or the weight of a bomb would be sufficient to upset the delicate balance of the ship.

But with this pot-shot, courtesy ended. The next day the Frenchman came up with a rifle. The German brought up his own gunner—with an automatic shot-gun. Soon they were potting at each other with machine guns. The war in the air was on.

That first pot-shot was to affect the career of the blue-eyed stripling in the western college town eight thousand miles away. For Johnny Powell heard the whir of wings. The sound was destined to grow in his ears.

Accounts of the exploits of the airmen filtered into the town from time to time. There was Navarre, the smooth-faced French youth with fourteen planes to his credit; there was Guynemer, ace of aces, the twenty-year old pilot with the "face of a

"SPEED" POWELL INSPECTS HIS HOME MADE RACER WITH THE GIRL NEXT DOOR.

Wings.

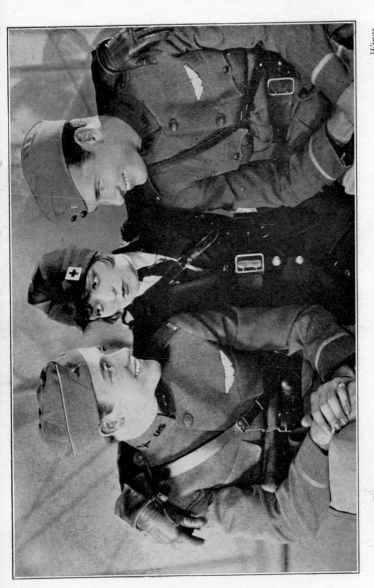

A Paramount Picture. *Wings.*
RE-UNITED AT THE FRONT—TWO GALAHADS OF THE AIR, AND THE GIRL WHO LOVED ONE OF THEM.

girl and the heart of a Frenchman." There
was Captain Ball, of the Royal Air Force,
who fought the German super-hawk, Immelman, in a prearranged duel in full sight
of the lines. There was Captain Boelke and
Baron von Richthofen, of the Imperial Flying Corps, Victor Chapman, Norman
Prince, Raoul Lufberry, Kiffin Rockwell, of
the Lafayette Escadrille.

Johnny Powell read every scrap of news
about these super-airmen. He knew the
legends current about them, their histories,
their methods of attack. He knew, for instance, that Immelman swooped down on his
prey from a great height, shooting as he
passed and that he never returned to attack
if the enemy plane were not brought down.

Navarre dashed straight for his enemy,
circled him and worried him with discon-
certing fire. And he always pursued his
enemy if he fled, buzzing over and above him
like an angry wasp, his machine gun popping.

Guynemer, of course, had the quickest eye
of them all; he had brought down three Ger-

man fliers in 150 seconds, the greatest military feat ever performed in the air. He used every form of attack, straight firing from the enemy's level, the deadly surprise dash from behind a cloud bank, the hawk-like swoop from above.

But it was all pretty remote.

Then in March of 1917, German U-boats sunk the *Vigilancia,* the *City of Memphis,* the *Illinois,* the *Healdton,* four American ships, and torpedoed the American freighter *Aztec* and the war was brought to Johnny's doorstep.

On April 2, 1917, the President, at eight in the evening, in the Capitol at Washington, told a tense Congress that:

"With a profound sense of the solemn and even tragical step I am taking . . . I advise that the Congress declare the recent course of the Imperial German Government to be in fact nothing less than war against the Government and People of the United States; that it formally accept the status of belligerent that has been thrust upon it. . . ."

The next day everything was changed.

Overnight the campus took a new complexion. They gathered in excited knots on the steps, in the hallways, along the walks. The air was vibrant with sensation. Lectures became pallid and commonplace. The business of going to school had become, of a minute, intolerably humdrum and workaday.

They scattered quickly enough; to the Coast Artillery, to the Officers' Training Camps, to the Naval Training Stations, to the Quartermaster Corps, to the Ambulance Sections. To the Presidio, to Camp Lewis, to Bremerton, to Allentown. The idea was to get into it right now. Classes tapered down to slender groups. The chemistry profs hurried away. The President was called to a Safety Council.

The hell of it was, Johnny Powell was only eighteen. He couldn't get into an officers' training camp. He couldn't get into anything—unless he lied about his age.

Everybody told him to stick. What the hell, he was too young—wait awhile.

His father said he wasn't to do anything at all. He was to keep right on with his education and when the time came he would be all the better equipped for whatever service he should be called to.

"Promise me, son," his mother said, with tears standing in her eyes, "that you won't do anything." And Johnny said he wouldn't.

He stood it pretty well for a while, what with everybody patting him on the back and telling him it took more courage to stick than to fly off at the first note of the bugle.

But one morning his eye caught an item in the paper that made his heart bounce. Not a large item, but one that was to change the direction of his life; it was an announcement of the opening of an examining station in Seattle for candidates for the American Air Service. Johnny went out of the house with his eyes shining.

Mary saw him cranking up the car.

"Where you going?"

"Oh, just for a little ride," said Johnny cautiously.

"Take me?"

He studied her for a second. "All right, jump in."

She never knew Johnny to drive so swiftly or so well. It was supreme pleasure just to ride with him, so effortlessly did he handle the yellow roadster. They went skimming along, bare-headed, shirt-sleeved in the open car in the morning sun, slipping by everyone on the road, Mary's dress ballooning in the wind.

Not until they were in Seattle did Mary know where they were going. Johnny parked the car in front of the municipal building with Mary in it and said he would be gone "quite a few minutes." Mary waited two hours.

There were two other boys from Temple in the ante-room when Johnny went in. One was Herman Schwimpf and the other was Dave Armstrong. Johnny didn't mind Herman, he was kind of a funny-looking, harmless bird—was putting himself through college by night-work in a garage—but he did somehow resent the presence of Armstrong.

It seemed that wherever he went Armstrong was in ahead of him.

Armstrong was called first because his name began with "A." Johnny learned then what he was to learn over and over again, that in this man's army it was a great help to be near the top of the alphabet.

It made him restive to see Armstrong walk in before him but he tried to comfort himself with the thought that maybe Armstrong wouldn't survive the tests. They were pretty severe, he'd heard. They made you hold the points of a needle between your thumb and forefinger and then shot off a pistol unexpectedly in your ear to see if you'd flinch and draw blood. Maybe that was all bunk.

"Powell!"

"Yes, Sir."

"Step in, Powell."

Johnny followed the uniformed figure inside.

"Age?"

"Nineteen."

"What do you weigh, Powell?"

"Hundred and forty-two."

"Take off your clothes."

"Now this," said the doctor to his assistant, when Johnny stood stripped to the skin, "is the type of youngster we want."

"Yes?" returned the other. "Probably has a thick ear drum or a tobacco heart or hernia or something. These likely looking ones usually have something the matter."

The examining doctor put a stethoscope to Johnny's heart and lungs, tapped his chest and upper back with a practised forefinger, wrapped a rubber bandage around his arm and took his blood pressure, calling off to his assistant with a pad, "Normal—Normal—Normal."

"When the chair stops spinning focus your eyes on the wall." In vain Johnny tried to fix his swimming eyes on the wall when the chair came to rest while the doctor, his face an inch away, peered intently into them. The instant they stopped he clicked a stop-watch. "Nystagmus—to the right—normal."

Johnny read lighted charts in a dark room

with right eye and his left eye and with both eyes; he listened to a watch tick at varying distances from his ear and he balanced on one foot with his eyes closed. In other words they tested his eyes, his ears, his heart, his balance and they took specimens of his blood and water.

"That's all, Powell. You can put your clothes on."

"Yes, Sir."

The first intimation that Mary had of the business going on inside was when she saw David Armstrong coming down the steps of the building.

"Hello," he said, "what in the world are you doing here?"

"Waiting for Johnny Powell."

"He ought to be out any minute, he was dressing when I left."

"Dressing?" queried Mary.

"They put us through quite a course of sprouts," said Dave, "I didn't realize before what it took to make an aviator."

"Aviator?"

"If there's anything wrong with you they'll surely find it out." David walked toward his car unaware that he had imparted the secret of Johnny's trip.

The light broke over Mary. So *that* was it. Johnny was trying to get into the Air Service. No wonder he didn't want to take her along. No wonder . . . but what would his mother say? . . .

When Johnny came down the steps, Mary looked up at him inquiringly—as almost any girl would have done who had been left parked for two hours in an open car at the curb—but Johnny vouchsafed no explanation and Mary did not demand to know.

There were two reasons in Johnny's mind why he did not tell Mary what he had done. In the first place, he was afraid she might let it slip to his mother. And secondly, he did not know if he had passed the laboratory tests and it would be humiliating to acknowledge later to Mary that he had failed.

Mary divined what was going on in his mind and was satisfied to let him tell her in his own good time. One thought occurred to her almost immediately. She didn't have a good photograph of herself. At least not one good enough for Johnny to carry with him when he went off to war. And surely he'd ask for one. Yes, she must have some decent pictures taken. . . .

From the day of his examination Johnny Powell walked about the house with a tiny, brilliant point of light glittering in his eyes and his head lifted in the manner of one who hears, faint and far away, the whir of wings.

His suppressed excitement communicated itself inevitably to his mother, who, puzzled and apprehensive, divined that something momentous was afoot in Johnny's life.

She did not need to, for the events of the next weeks brought out the truth.

Professor Powell had been for some weeks troubled about his son. He felt that the hour was approaching when he must come to grips with him about the car. The old gentleman had unfortunately overheard some characterize his son as "wild" and it bothered him not a little. Surely his son wasn't wild. A little high-powered perhaps, for Temple, a little thoughtless but not *wild*.

But when one or two of his friends spoke to him on the street he came to realize in what light Johnny was generally esteemed. In fact it gradually came home to him that Speed Powell was held to be the wildest boy in town.

The gentle gray-haired professor was mightily disturbed. That yellow car! He'd have to speak to his son.

On Tuesday of that week Professor Powell received a notice that his son had failed three out of five of his trimester examinations and had, in consequence, been placed on probation. The professor put the blue card on his desk and tightened his lips.

On Wednesday he inadvertently opened an envelope addressed to John Powell Jr., and discovered it to be a notice to appear in traffic court for violation of ordinance 113-A. Johnny, it transpired, had opened his cut-out in the very heart of town and the traffic cop down at the bank intersection had spotted his number.

On the very same day Johnny's mother found in the coat pocket of the suit which she was about to send out to be pressed for him, a notice that he was to appear before Judge Seth P. McIntyre to answer a charge of violating traffic ordinance 113-B. He had been travelling, it appeared on the ticket, at the rate of 55 miles an hour in a twenty mile zone.

Johnny's parents had a long discussion *in camera*. Of a certainty the boy was running wild.

But there was more to come. That evening Judge McIntyre, who lived in the same block and who was an old friend of Professor Powell's, dropped in for a chat. "About that yellow racer of your son's," he remarked casually during the course of the conversation, did Professor Powell really think it was a good thing for the boy?

The reason he was asking, Judge McIntyre said, was because Johnny had been in the traffic court twice on speeding charges, had been let off with suspended sentences and if he turned up a third time, he, Judge

McIntyre, would have no other recourse but to accept the recommendation of the police and take away his driving license.

At this point the doorbell rang and Professor Powell found himself waited upon by another caller. It proved to be Mr. Witherspoon who ran the vegetable market over on Tenth and Grove.

Reluctant as he was to state the object of his visit, Mr. Witherspoon felt, he said, that he ought to bring the matter to Professor Powell's attention. Day before yesterday, Mr. Witherspoon's delivery wagon was standing in front of his store. A car came dashing around the corner of Grove and the driver opened his cut-out just as he passed the horse. The horse became unmanageable and backed clear through the plate glass window, and did quite a little damage to his stock.

Mr. Witherspoon had a new front put in and the stock replaced but he couldn't help but feel, he said, that the expense, or at least part of the expense ought to be borne by the person responsible for the accident. He didn't want to trouble the professor about it but the car was a yellow roadster. . . .

"You may be assured," said Professor Powell grimly, "that if the responsibility for the accident lies with my son you will be properly indemnified."

All three in the room heard the roar of an open cut-out coming down the street. Lights flashed along the side of the house and there was a banging of garage doors. The next moment the front door burst open and the subject of the conversation walked into the hall.

"Oh, son!" Professor Powell called.

"Yes, Sir?"

"Could you step in here just a minute, please?"

Johnny Powell walked into the living room.

What ensued thereafter was painful to both Professor Powell and to his son. It had to be gone through with sooner or later, and Johnny's father hardened himself for the business. A timid man, really, when it came to laying down the law, he felt that he ought to seize this moment, when the subject was more or less critical and he had the moral support of the two men in the room with him.

Johnny readily admitted the truth of the charges, but appeared to show neither embarrassment nor concern. Only when his father got down to the crux of the matter did he appear to take much interest.

"I have come to the conclusion," said his father, "that having this car of yours is unwise. I believe that if that distraction were removed you would apply your mind to more serious endeavors. I'm afraid I must forbid you to take it out of the garage——"

What! Take the *Shooting Star* away from him! It was his car. Dr. MacRoberts had given it to him. And he had fixed it up out of his allowance money!

Yes, but about the window and the fines. His father would have to take care of those. And as Johnny very well knew, the Powells could not afford money for that sort of thing——

Well, Johnny said, he would work those out some way.

But about the probation card. It wasn't only the reckless driving, it was the fact that his scholarship was going to pieces. The only thing he seemed to be thinking of nowadays was that car. No, it would be best if he didn't have that car, at least for a time anyway.

But to Johnny, the ignominy of having his car taken away from him, the *Shooting Star* that everybody knew about, was insupportable. He couldn't think of facing his friends. They would, he foresaw, kid the pants off him. Besides it *was* his car. *His* car. His voice rose. He flared into open rebellion.

Here Professor Powell faced a hard task. It was the first time he had ever approached an open breach with his son. Yet he foresaw that if he were to packpaddle now, and in the presence of these men, he would lose permanent control of him. He must impose his will upon the boy.

"My son," he began in a steady voice,

"you're on the wrong path. You're headed for trouble. You're slighting your studies, you're neglecting your home, you're distressing your mother. You appear to be spending the greater part of your time flying about in that yellow car. And in violating the laws——"

"But, Dad—"

"I want you to listen to me, son. I've only just come to realize what everyone else seems to know: that you've gotten completely out of hand. You're becoming a wilful, headstrong, reckless youth. You're travelling at entirely too fast a clip. In fact it's become evident to me that you and your car constitute a menace to the streets of this community——"

Johnny snorted.

"——and I intend to put an immediate stop to it before you do yourself or someone else serious injury. Do you understand?"

Johnny gave his father a hostile nod.

"Very well then. *You are not to take that car out of the garage again until I give you permission.*"

"But, Dad——"

"That is final."

"But, Dad," Johnny cried passionately, "you can't take it away from me. It's *mine!*"

Professor Powell, very pale and still, looked at his son.

"I forbid you to set foot in it again."

"I won't promise!"

"Son!" Professor Powell was on his feet. "You refuse to obey your father?"

The two faced each other; Johnny, flushed and quivering; his father, white and silent. Johnny's mother, drawn by the hot words passing between the two, had come to the doorway, stood, unnoticed, an unhappy witness to the deadlock between father and son.

The ring of the doorbell broke faintly in upon the tense silence in the room. Johnny's mother turned and went to the front door.

"Where do I sign?" they heard her ask.

A moment later she re-entered the room holding out a telegram to Johnny. "It's for you, son," she said in a voice charged with alarm. To her knowledge Johnny had never received a telegram before in his life.

Johnny took the telegram, looked at it, looked at his mother and started to slip it into his pocket as if it were of no moment.

"Aren't you going to open it?"

Johnny turned to his mother with a desperate, trapped look. Something told him that this was going to be a bad time to open that telegram. Still there was no way out.

Hesitantly he worked open the flap:

"Herewith notice your acceptance as Private 1st. Class Aviation Section, Signal Reserve Corps. You will proceed directly to Berkeley Calif. and report upon arrival to Commandant School of Military Aeronautics. . . ."

The look on his face betrayed him to his mother. She reached for the yellow slip.

Slowly, very slowly, the import of the telegram came upon her. When she raised her head her eyes were bright with tears.

"Oh, my son. My blessed, blessed son."

They were in each other's arms.

Professor Powell took the telegram from between her fingers. He adjusted his glasses and bent over the message. With brave, resolute dignity he addressed the two men in the room.

"Gentlemen, my son is going to war."

He turned away. They found their hats and stole quietly from the room.

At nine-thirty that evening Sylvia Lewis was seated at the spindle-legged escritoire in the Kappa house den penning an inscription upon the back of a small square photograph of herself. When she had finished, she held it up for a second to read the lines, and then, apparently satisfied, she blotted the ink and began to fit the picture into a tiny silver miniature case. David was coming in to say goodbye. He was leaving for ground school tonight.

One of the girls put her head in the door. "Your caller's arrived," she announced.

"Tell him to come in," said Sylvia without looking up.

She heard the door open and close and

when she did look up she saw not David but Johnny Powell.

"Oh," she exclaimed. Instinctively, she snapped the case shut and covered it with her hand.

The gesture betrayed her to Johnny. He stood smiling at her confusion. She felt the blood rising in her face.

"Let me see," he demanded mischievously.

"No—no——"

"Let me see—" His hand was over hers and he was separating the locket from her fingers.

"Johnny, please—please——!"

It was no use. The case was in his hands and he was opening it. Sylvia stood helplessly watching him.

She saw a sudden happiness overspread his features when he beheld the miniature.

"You knew I was going away!"

She looked at him not knowing what to say.

"And you knew I'd want a picture—to carry with me. Gosh, Sylvia, it's *lovely*."

Sylvia stared at him in bewilderment. It

dawned upon her suddenly that Johnny had
divined that the picture was for *him*.

"But I—but——"

"You don't know what it means for me to
have a picture of you—with me. Why, it
means everything."

"But, Johnny,——"

"Sylvia, it was wonderful of you to think
of it! I'll keep it with me—all the time."
He gazed raptly at the little blonde head in
the locket.

Poor Sylvia. She could never tell him
now.

"Will you write to me, Sylvia," he begged
eagerly, "as often as I write to you?"

"Of course, Johnny."

But when he tried to kiss her goodbye,
she held him off.

Armstrong heard about it when he came
in half an hour later.

"Let him keep it," he said, "if it makes
him happy. I don't care so long as I know
I have you, Sylvia."

"He mustn't know," she murmured
thoughtfully.

And when it was time for David to go Sylvia offered him her lips, freely and without restraint.

Mary Preston had a picture all ready for Johnny when he came to say goodbye.

"So long," he said, "you can have the *Shooting Star* now, I guess. Only don't wreck it because I may want it when I come back. And, for gosh sakes, don't be running 'er with the choke on. You foul up the plugs."

Mary, whose heart was bursting, could only nod dumbly. He never even asked her for a picture.

When he was gone, when it was an indisputable fact that he was gone, when the train had left and the Powells had come back from the station and the lights in their house were turned off, Mary crept over into Johnny's silent, empty back yard, climbed into the *Shooting Star,* put her head down on the wheel that had known the touch of his hands, and wept.

And Johnny Powell went happily off to war with another girl's picture in a silver locket around his neck. A picture of a blonde-headed girl with a tender legend written on the back. A legend that ran:

"To David Armstrong, with heart's dearest love,

SYLVIA."

That's how Johnny Powell went to war.

PART II

"LOOKIT THE EARS ON 'IM"

PART II

THE tanned, all-wise members of the graduating class of the United States Army School of Military Aeronautics at Berkeley, California, surveyed the incoming squadron with sardonic relish. It was a gruelling, precarious journey down to where they stood and they knew it.

"Lookit the ears on 'em. . . ."

"Geeroosalem, lookit 'at sojer boy. . . ."

"There's a flier—lookit his ears. . . ."

"If there isn't Immelman hisself. . . ."

"Lookit his EARS. . . ."

Under a gentle barrage of ground school humor, Speed Powell, David Armstrong, Herman Schwimpf and the other ill-at-ease arrivals were marched to the quartermaster's window to draw their equipment. An

53

hour later Johnny surveyed the broad tan toes of his issue shoes and reflected that he was in the army.

The course in Military Aeronautics at Berkeley, as the members of Squadron Fourteen were soon to discover, was no midnight stroll with a beautiful maiden on a scented summer's eve.

They entered, these hand-picked youngster's, in squadrons of ninety and they graduated, at the end of eight weeks of intensive training, in squadrons of thirty. Only the mentally alert survived the course. Of the cream of youth that entered ground school, the Air Service wanted only the *crème de la crème*.

A completely-trained aviator cost the Government, so it was said, $50,000. That was the sum that it required to educate, instruct and equip a pilot for the highly-specialized service of military flying. It behooved the War Department, therefore, to select for training only those youngsters with flawless physical make-ups and perfect balance and who were between the ages of 19 and 25. For, as the French had learned from their pilots, "under nineteen they are too bold; over twenty-five they are too prudent."

From the numbers of eager youths who met the age limits and satisfied the physical requirements it was necessary to select those who were mentally suited to the task. It was part of the purpose of the ground schools, therefore, to weed out the unpromising, the slower-witted, the unfit. The process of elimination was cruel, arbitrary and often unfair.

Many a youngster who might have made an excellent pilot, given the chance, never set foot in a plane because he missed four questions in a meteorological examination. Many another Guynemer, another Fonck, or another Lufbery perished in the first few weeks of ground school. Many an ace died aborning.

But it was war-time. The school was run at top-speed and under high pressure. Pilots had to be trained for the new air fleets, and in an incredibly short space. No time to nurse along weak sisters; no leisure to re-examine failures.

Besides, the Air Service authorities pointed out, if you let a doubtful man through he'd likely kill himself later on, or crack up a ship worth $15,000. Why take the risk?

The flying cadets at Berkeley began the day on the run and ended it on the run. They were bugled out of bed at six in the morning and they were turned in at ten at night. There were long, hot hours of drilling under whip-tongued officers on the sun-baked parade ground.

There were rapid fire lectures on military discipline, courtesy and law; on articles of war; on signalling, radio, ballistics, gunnery, map-reading, meteorology, aerodynamics, internal combustion motors, carburetors and ignition.

There was a grim succession of weekly examinations bristling with questions like:

"How do each of the following effect the lift of a wing?

(a) Area.

(b) Angle of incidence.

(c) Velocity."

"Does the feed arm operating stud boss leave the channel of the feed arm at the end of the backward motion of the rack in the Lewis Machine Gun?"

And:

"Assume that you have a sketch which has no north and south line shown and you have no compass. Explain in full how you would orient the sketch."

Each week saw its heart-cracking moments in front of the bulletin board when the grades were posted. John Powell overheard a cadet trying to comfort Herman Schwimpf the day after a gunnery final.

"Hard luck, ol' man. I'm sorry as hell. But, Lord, it was a tough one. Don't see how the hell I ever got through myself. Just luck is all.

"Sure the artillery is O.K.—or an ambulance section. If I was you I'd get into an ambulance section.

"Get overseas faster. Probably before we will. You're pretty lucky at that. Might

of got bumped off your first solo. Sure . . .
ah, buck up ol' scout . . . buck up . . . I
wouldn't take it so hard . . . hell. . . ."

Johnny heard afterward that Herman had
gone overseas as a mechanic attached to the
39th Aero Squadron.

No one ever had to comfort Johnny Powell. His compelling nature was supremely
adapted to any survival-of-the-fittest campaign. He went sailing his untroubled way
through the course with never a thought of
disaster.

The very instruments that had brought
him into disrepute in Temple now stood him
in splendid stead. Every hour he had spent
on the *Shooting Star* now counted in his
favor, for he knew more about the action,
principle and operation of gas engines than
any cadet in the class.

At the end of eight weeks Johnny could
strip down a Lewis gun to its myriad parts
and assemble it, lightning-fast, blind-folded.
He was breaking twenty out of twenty-five
clay pigeons on the traps. He had the oiling,
cooling, feeding and exhaust systems of the

A Paramount Picture. *Wings.*

WORKING HARD FOR COMMISSIONS, WITH THE ROAR OF WAR JUST OUTSIDE.

A Paramount Picture.

THE SQUADRON OF AIRMEN AT MESS IN A RUINED CHATEAU, WITHIN RANGE OF
ENEMY GUNS.

Wings.

Hispano-Suiza and Gnome rotary motor down to a swift and accurate explanation. He knew cirrus and cumulus clouds and how to spot the North Star and how to write a military letter and address a superior officer. And he could make up his cot, brush his teeth, roll his puttees and be on the line in a split-second. In the weekly examination lists the name of Cadet Powell was invariably inside the first five.

His sensitive fingers had taken so readily to a telegraph key that he became the fastest operator in the squadron. He was clicking off forty words of International Morse code a minute, which, except for the sending of a young ship's wireless operator who was taking the course, was the speediest in the school.

The wireless test was the final one at Berkeley. Simple enough in itself—the cadet was called up before an examiner, seated at a wireless key, handed a printed message and ordered to put it on the wire—it represented, nevertheless, the stiffest hurdle of the course.

More cadets failed on wireless than on all of the other tests combined. Many a man who had gone sailing smoothly down the weeks crumpled up in that brief three minutes at the key. It wasn't that a knowledge of wireless was of such paramount importance to a flier; it was essential, of course, that he be able to flash messages from his plane above the battle lines, but that wasn't the real significance of the test at this time. It was the one test of nerve in the entire course. From the standpoint of the officers there were but two kinds of cadets; those who went to pieces in a pinch and those who tightened up in a pinch. Well, the wireless test was a pinch. It would damn well bring out which kind you were. The men who tightened up in the pinches were the ones who made fliers. They were the ones the Air Service was after.

There is scarcely a sixteenth of an inch clearance between the polished contact points of a wireless key. A nervous hand does not click off clear, crisp code over so delicately adjusted an instrument. The result is usually a blurring of dots and dashes, a stuttering and incoherent message.

If a cadet is nervous his nervousness translates itself to his hands. His palms sweat and his fingers are unsteady. Any inner agitation is therefore inevitably communicated to the wireless key.

An attack of nerves before the wireless test was generally fatal. It was usually the sober, thinking type who was subject to such an attack. When he stopped to realize that this was the last barrier standing between himself and his chance to fly, he was apt to become conscious of the great importance of the moment. His future hopes were all to be determined in the brief three minutes at the key. Those three minutes began to assume gigantic proportions. Suppose he should fail! He was allowed only five mistakes. God, that was a slim margin. They said you didn't get a second trial either. Hell. For the first time he felt the moisture in the palms of his hands. . . .

The careless, confident type like Speed Powell, on the other hand, never gave it a second thought.

Johnny was seated on his cot folding his laundry away in his locker trunk on the night before the wireless final. He observed a group gathering about Armstrong's cot but he paid little attention inasmuch as he wasn't at all concerned about him. He would have felt an unholy glee if Armstrong had flunked out, but he had no feeling for him other than a vague hostility.

Presently a cadet named Arnold, Johnny never did know his first name, detached himself from the group and strolled over to Johnny's cot. He was a cool, astute youngster with much of Johnny's irreverence for the dignity of superior officers and no special regard for discipline.

"Going to knock it cold, eh?" he saluted Johnny.

"Hope so," Johnny assented.

"Boy, you're lucky."

"How so?"

"To have wireless licked like that. Look at Armstrong."

"What's the matter with Armstrong?"

"Gone all to hell."

Johnny looked up in surprise. Armstrong? Gone to hell? The steady-going Armstrong?

"Sure," said Arnold. "He got to thinking about it and it's got his goat."

"Yeah?" Johnny showed a mild interest. So the old boy might flunk out after all. He could not suppress a feeling of mild elation over the downfall of his rival.

"Damn shame," proceeded Arnold, eyeing Johnny, "he's a hell of a good scout, Armstrong. Do anything for you."

"Yeah?" Johnny was unimpressed.

"It's not fair," the other burst out, "to kick a man out on that one test. He'd make a damn good pilot."

"Well, maybe he'll get through all right," Johnny suggested.

"Through hell! He's got the shakes! Hand's trembling like a leaf. Can't even hold a key."

"That's tough," Johnny agreed.

"Say," demanded Arnold, "do you know what you ought to do?"

"Nope."

"You ought to take his test for him."

"Me?"

"Sure. You're the shark of the squadron. You could pull it off and nobody'd know the difference."

"How?" said Johnny, astonished.

"Well, they're going to have two examiners, see. And they split the squadron up into two lines, alphabetically. When they call Armstrong's name all you have to do is to step up and take his place."

"But they'd recognize me."

"No, they won't. They're a couple of professional operators brought in for the exam. They've never seen anybody in the squadron before. All they do is call off the names, listen to the test and mark down the grades. Hell, the boys worked this stunt in the last three squadrons."

"Well, since you like Armstrong so much why don't you substitute for him yourself?"

"I would," declared Arnold warmly, "but my name begins with the same initial. We'll be in the same line and probably be called about the same time."

"Well, why the hell should *I*—" began Johnny when he suddenly found himself looking up into a semi-circle of expectant faces. He realized then that here was a plot to pull Armstrong through and that they were looking to him as the key figure.

"Go ahead, Powell," one of them urged, "you can get away with it. And think what it means to him."

The cot next to Powell's was occupied by "Deacon" Groves, a lank, horse-faced cadet from a Southern Theological Seminary. The Deacon had been listening quietly to the conversation and now came up on his elbow.

"Are you fellows crazy?" he demanded. "Trying to pull a trick like that? You'll both get fired out of the Service if you aren't careful. If they don't find you out I think I ought to report you myself."

One of the circle, a great-shouldered, heavy-coupled lad from the North, a former

Washington oarsman, swung about and glared down at the Deacon.

"If you open your yap about this," he growled, "I'll snap your spine."

The Deacon subsided.

Something about the loyalty of these men for one of the brothers in distress got to Johnny.

He got up and walked over to Armstrong's cot. He put his arm gently across the drooping shoulders of the dejected figure.

"Don't worry, old man," said Johnny. "I'll see you through."

There were several pairs of sleepless eyes in the barracks that night but none of them belonged to Johnny Powell. Having made up his mind to it, he would go through with it with a serene confidence in his own destiny, but he thought it a kind of ironical turn of fate that he should find himself jockeyed into pulling off a mad piece of skullduggery for Armstrong, of all people.

The other cadets who were in on the conspiracy worried far more over the outcome than did Johnny himself. There was some-

thing splendid in the spectacle of a cadet
risking his commission, his name and his
flying career for another. And what a cool
customer this Powell was! It was enough
of a nerve-strain to take your own wireless
test, to say nothing of taking it under the
double jeopardy of arrest and exposure.

It did not seem to Johnny that there was
any moral aspect to the plot. All was fair
in love and war, wasn't it? And besides it
was a kind of game. Anything you could do
to outwit your superior officers.

It had never occurred to him to cheat in
an examination at school. There you were
working to your own advantage. Here you
were doing it for a different purpose. Men
did all kinds of things to get into the service; they lied stoutly about their ages, they
concealed physical defects, they practised all
sorts of mild deceptions. But they were
kind of glorious deceptions because the men
were struggling to offer themselves to their
country for war. They were fighting for the
chance to get killed.

Once in France nobody asked you how

you got there. It didn't matter how you got to the front just so you got to the front and got your crack at the Heinies.

Besides, Johnny knew it was in his power to see David through his trouble. He would have felt a hell of a lot guiltier afterwards, he knew, if he turned his back on him now and refused to save him. As it was he was quite content in his mind that he was doing the right thing. The finer ethical aspects of the matter escaped him.

At ten-thirty in the morning the squadron was divided in half and formed in parallel lines outside the two entrances of the wireless building. A sergeant inside the doorway relayed the names outside.

"Armstrong!"

A cadet detached himself from the line, slipped through the door, walked the length of the room and presented himself to the examiner seated behind a table at the far end. He was a spare little man with a bald head and pale, unseeing eyes.

"Armstrong?"

The cadet saluted.

"Try the key."

There was too much play between the contact points. The cadet tightened the screw expertly.

The examiner adjusted his head phones and handed over a code card beginning MG7SW FRAZ4 T9KL2 VXQBO. . . .

"Start whenever you're ready," he ordered, glancing at the watch lying face open on the table in front of him.

"— — — —. — — ... — .. — —
.. —. .— . — .. — — ..
... — — —. .— . — . —
.. .. — — —"

The dots and dashes came through the phones in an even rhythmic flow. Never once did the tempo change or the wrist falter.

When the candidate clicked off the series of triple dots signalling the end of the message the examiner looked up with an impassive face.

"Arnold," he called, already concerned with the next name on the list. "Arnold next."

The cadet walked briskly out of the door.

Around the corner of the building Armstrong was pacing up and down. He looked up at Johnny with a face stiff with suspense and eyes bright with anxiety.

"Duck soup," said Johnny briefly.

The tall cadet slumped down on the sunsplashed steps of the building. Burying his face in his hands he began to sob hysterically.

"Everything's all right, old man," Johnny said with surprising tenderness, "everything is all right now . . . don't . . . don't . . . you're through ol' man . . . nothing to worry about now. . . ."

"I'll never forget this," said Armstrong in a low voice, "as long as I live."

The next morning the skipper of the squadron read an order:

"The following named cadets will proceed immediately to Rockwell Field, San Diego, California, and will report at once to the Commanding Officer for assignment to duty. Abrams, Armstrong, Arnold . . . Powell . . ."

The surviving members of Squadron 14 were marched off to the final review on the parade grounds.

When the final note of the bugle had died down and the last command had rung across the field and the ranks broke up, Johnny Powell saw Armstrong spring into his mother's arms and saw his gray-haired father take him pridefully by the elbow, and Johnny decided that any risk he had taken was worth it.

A new batch of flying cadets turned up on the grounds the day that Squadron 14 left.

"Look at the ears on 'em," observed Johnny as he passed out of the gate.

Meanwhile affairs had been going forward in Johnny's home town. The war fever had taken full possession of Temple and everyone was scurrying about doing something patriotic.

Mrs. Bell Thomas, the wealthiest woman in town, had conceived the notion of organizing and equipping a branch of the Women's Motor Corps of America. It was her intention to send a Temple unit overseas as she had read that Bryn Mawr and Wellesley had done.

Driving a light duty truck in France wasn't nearly so romantic as nursing but it was quite as useful. The girls of the Motor Corps drove supplies from the base warehouses in Paris to the canteens and to the base hospitals. And sometimes, after a big offensive they were pressed into ambulance service.

Of the thirty-odd society girls in Temple who responded to Mrs. Bell Thomas's call, Mary Preston proved to be the only one who could operate a Ford. In the days when she worked side by side with Johnny in his backyard she had come to know a flivver backwards and forwards and she had, under Johnny's expert tuition, learned to drive like a professional.

Mary Preston was made the head of the little unit of five that Mrs. Bell Thomas sent back to New York for overseas training. In New York Mary slept with other members of the Women's Motor Corps in the rooms above the Corps' garage in Long Island City.

After a month in the clinics, two weeks with the insane on Ward's Island learning to handle shell-shocked, and a month in the garages, she passed her first-aid, driving and drilling tests and won her insignia.

She looked very boyish in her trim serge uniform with the visored cap, the tunic, the belt, the leather puttees and the short skirt. They wore riding breeches beneath the skirt; the skirt buttoned up the front and could be taken off at a moment's notice for motorcycle side-car driving.

Down at Rockwell Field Johnny Powell received a snap-shot of Mary in uniform, with a little note written in Mary's girlish hand on the back:

"I'll beat you to France yet, Johnny boy."

"The little son-of-a-gun," said Johnny.

Rockwell Field was enveloped in a flood of hazy sunlight, the incessant drone of propellers and a cloud of airplanes, circling, alighting and taking off. High up over San

Diego Harbor a plane, like a silver fish, looped and spun in the sunlight. The soft pattern of light and sound was broken periodically by the sharp rattle of machine gun fire from the target range.

"Just get in?"

A tall cadet with darkly tanned face and hands uncurled himself from the cot where he was lying and sat up when Johnny and David came into the tent. Their arms were loaded with bedding and flying togs, new issue that they had just drawn at the quartermaster's window.

"Yep," said Johnny. "Is this all right?" he asked, depositing his equipment on the empty cot nearest the door.

"Sure, anywhere. Well, your grief's all ahead of you," said the cadet. "My name's White," he said, standing up and offering his hand with a friendly smile. He exhibited none of the sharp superiority usually accorded the novices by the older fliers. "I expect we'll see a lot of each other."

"Powell's my name," said Johnny with a

A Paramount Picture.
CLARA'S EFFORT TO SAVE POWELL FROM COURT MARTIAL, RESULTS IN DISCOVERY AND DISGRACE.

Wings.

A Paramount Picture.

THE BIG PUSH OF INFANTRY UP TOWARD THE FRONT LINES.

Wings.

sudden liking for the cadet, "and this is Armstrong."

"Buddies?"

Johnny nodded his head.

"Here, hang your stuff up here," said White.

David was looking at a leather flying helmet hanging on a nail in the tent-pole. A miniature ivory elephant dangled from a red silk cord sewn to the ear-flap.

"What's the idea?" he inquired. "Mascot or something?"

"Sure," said White, "luck charm, mascot, talisman, anything. That's Mike's," he explained, "not mine."

"Most of the fliers carry lucky pieces?" Johnny inquired.

"Practically all of 'em. Except me."

"You don't believe in them?"

"Not me." A curiously fixed, fatalistic expression came across White's face and settled in his eyes.

"Why not?"

"Oh, it's just a superstition. I don't think it makes any difference——"

"Cadet White!" A sergeant stood in the doorway of the tent.

"Here."

"Report to the solo field. Stage Eight."

"Going out on cross-country," White explained when the non-com had gone.

"That's the last stage, isn't it?" Johnny asked.

"Yep. I'm getting through," he said, picking up his goggles. "You boys'll have to salute me next week."

"Lieutenant White?" said Johnny.

"That's right. Only a couple or more trips now and I'll be on my way."

The shadows of airplanes kept flitting, like birds of dark omen, across the white canvas top of the tent.

"Nope," he said, turning around to look at them just before he went through the doorway, "I don't believe in mascots. I never noticed that it made any difference. They kill about three a week here. And that's not so many at that. Hell, down at Fort Worth they're knocking 'em off five a week. It just depends if your number's in."

The shadow of a plane passed over his face as he stood half in the tent entrance.

"Nope," he said. "Luck or no luck. Charm or no charm. When your time comes you're going to get it." He was gone.

Somehow, the faint, friendly, honest quality of his smile hung in the air of the tent like a blessing.

Johnny and David busied themselves getting their things in order. The truck pulled up with their locker trunks.

"Three a week," repeated Johnny as he unfolded his blankets and began to make his cot.

"I suppose he means they average three accidents a week," said Dave. "Some weeks perhaps nobody gets hurt."

"Have you got a mascot?" Johnny asked, a little timidly.

"Yes, but you'll think it's a funny one."

"What is it?"

David went into the top tray of his trunk

and found a little furry rabbit, a tiny bat-
tered toy with staring, shoe-button eyes and
a lop ear.

"It was the first plaything I ever had,"
he said. "My mother gave it to me when
I was a tiny baby. I happened to see it lying in my mother's sewing basket the night
I left. I picked it up and brought it along,
just for luck."

David slipped the rabbit into the breast
pocket of his shirt and buttoned down the
flap. "When I go into the air this goes with
me," he said. "How about yourself?" he
inquired. "Do you carry anything?"

"Yep." Johnny's hand strayed to the
neckband of his shirt and then as if remem-
bering himself he suddenly drew it away.

David saw the movement. So the silver
locket with Sylvia's miniature had become
Johnny's lucky piece.

"As a matter of fact," said David easily,
"you really don't need a mascot, Johnny."

"How so?"

"You're lucky anyway. Nothing will ever
happen to you. You're that kind. But

I'm not. I—need—all—the—luck—there—is—going."

A dark shadow flashed across the tent roof. From far out on the field came the sound of a terrific explosion. It was like the crashing report of a small cannon going off in your ear. Neither David nor Johnny had heard a plane plunge into the earth before, and the sound was new—and terrible. It brought them to their feet.

A motorcycle coughed, started up and went down the road. Through the panel of light in the doorway they saw the ambulance careening across the field. Johnny started out. David caught his arm.

"You're not supposed to run to a crash."

"That's right," said Johnny.

They could see the crumpled mass of wreckage on the far corner of the landing field over toward Point Loma. The tail stuck upwards out of the earth, like the white shaft over a grave.

From outside the tent they could hear quiet voices.

"Must have fainted . . ."

"Caught in an air pocket probably . . ."

"If he'd had ten more feet . . . She was coming out of it, did you notice her nose coming up? . . ."

"I'll bet that was Fifty-two. She's got a heavy left wing. Always trying to fall off. Break your arm trying to keep her up . . ."

"Well, there's ten thousand dollars for the folks . . ."

It was an hour later, perhaps, when a motorcycle pulled up in front of the tent and a sergeant stepped out of the side-car.

"Cadet White live here?"

"Yes."

"Get his effects together. The truck'll pick 'em up this afternoon."

David and Johnny collected White's things with hesitant fingers. They were "effects" now. His comb, his brushes, his toilette things, his tooth brush—still damp from the morning. They rolled them in a towel and put them away in his sturdy little green locker trunk with his socks and his underclothes and his pajamas.

A minute before, White had stood there

smiling at them. Now he was a bloody bundle on a cot in the hospital. The joy-stick had driven right through his stomach, a corporal told them later.

But it was all too sudden. Things didn't happen as suddenly as that. You couldn't believe it.

They shuffled his letters together and tied them with a string. There was a picture of his mother in a leather case, a fountain pen, a trick wrist compass, a package of cigarettes.

"Listen, Johnny," David said, "if anything ever happens to me, will you do something for me?"

"Of course."

"Will you go through my things before they're sent home?"

"If you'll do the same for me."

So they made a compact.

They wished that the corporal had taken the cot out of the tent along with the rest of White's things. They could not get used to it that night. It stood there, silent and empty.

The giant searchlights from the tower played over the dark corners of the flying field. The outlines of the hangars loomed against the star-shot sky. Along the dead line stood the ghostly row of training ships, the whiteness of their spread wings a blur in the darkness. Across the harbor twinkled the lights of San Diego.

The two boys lay in the tent with the empty cot.

"Say, wasn't that a hell of a note about White today?"

"I believe he knew it was coming."

"How so?"

"The way he looked."

"Believe me, I don't go up without my mascot."

"Me neither."

Captain Foote, veteran dual instructor, regarded his new charge doubtfully from the front cockpit of his plane.

"Ever flown before?"

"No, sir."

"Well, climb in."

Powell buttoned the collar of his leather coat, fastened the strap of his helmet beneath his chin, slid his goggles over his eyes and swung himself into the back seat.

"Got your safety belt buckled?"

"Yes, sir."

"Keep your left hand on the joy-stick so's you can feel what I'm doing with it. But *don't* hang onto it."

"No, sir."

"Last week a cadet froze onto the controls and threw me into a spin. Had to knock him loose with the fire extinguisher. Damn nearly finished us both."

This here's kind of a tough egg, Johnny figured to himself.

"If you lose your nerve," continued the Captain, "freeze onto the cowl. And if you get sick, get sick outside the ship, see? Not inside."

"Yes, sir."

"Contact!"

A mechanic twisted the propeller, the motor took and the plane started across the field gathering speed. Slowly her tail came

off the ground, her nose coming down to
the level of the horizon, the wheels racing
along over the hard packed earth.

Suddenly the Captain pulled back the
stick and rocketed the ship fifty feet in the
air. To Johnny it seemed as if the earth
and his bowels were falling away together.
His senses were drowned in the roar of the
propeller, the heavy drumming of the motor
and the swift rush of air. For several minutes he fought off a sense of insecurity, of
panic at his first separation from the earth.

Gradually he became aware of the sense
of swift, skimming flight. The roar of the
propeller became music to his ears; the smell
of high-test gasoline and burnt castor oil
became incense in his nostrils.

Nobody is a born flier. Some can't fly
at all. Some take to it more quickly than
others. But nobody just picks up and flies.
You have to get used to it.

The Air Service set eight hours as the
time limit in which a cadet should learn
to fly. If he couldn't fly in eight hours,—

eight hours of thirty-minute practise flights a day with an instructor—he was transferred out of the service.

Captain Foote, as Johnny surmised was no fairy godmother. On a curve he would pound his ear and kick the rudder bar as a signal that they were skidding. He would jerk the stick out of his hands when they went into a wing slip.

"God Almighty!" he would yell when they got down on the ground. "When she starts to skid BANK HER UP. When she starts to slip TURN HER NOSE INTO IT."

"Yes, sir."

"If you don't show some improvement tomorrow I'll set you on the ground—for good."

Johnny's eyes glittered but he said nothing.

Nevertheless, on the sixth day, after Johnny had made five three point landings in a row—wheels and tail-skid touching the ground at the same instant—Foote turned around and eyed him appraisingly.

"How much time have you had with me now, Powell?" he inquired not unkindly.

"Three hours, sir."

"Think you can fly her alone?"

Johnny had hot and cold flashes. "Yes, sir," he said stoutly.

"Well, I'm going to turn you loose, son. Report to the solo field in the morning."

It was noised about the squadron that Speed Powell had been sent up to solo in three hours. *Three hours.* He certainly had nerve, that boy. Arnold took six hours. Armstrong eight.

After First Solo came a succession of special instructors and advanced flying stages. He learned to fly tight spirals, figure-eights around white pylons, and dead-stick-landings. He flew cross-country, to La Jolla, San Luis Rey and Fallbrook and he practised fish-tail landings into strange fields.

Tommy Andrews, Johnny's stunt instructor at Imperial Beach, said that Johnny was the sweetest flier he'd ever had in his ship. In his stunt solo Johnny had executed the usual routine of Immelman Turns, tail-spins and loops and then essayed a whipstall, a barrel-roll and an upside-down spin of his own.

"You've got a flare for aerial acrobatics," said Andrews when he came down. "You like it, don't you?"

"A lot," Johnny confessed.

"Like to instruct in it?"

Johnny shook his head.

"I'll recommend you if you want."

"Thanks, but I want to get overseas."

"So do we all," said Andrews with a short laugh, "but there aren't any planes for us. You'll get a lot more flying right here."

Johnny still shook his head.

"Well, all right," said Andrews, "I'll give you a pursuit rating if you like but you'll be lucky to get across."

"None of this flying on your back stuff for mine," someone said in the darkness of the flier's quarters that night. "You can have all the wing-overs you like. Bombing is the real dope. I want to drop eggs on Berlin."

Why anybody should choose to fly a great lumbering bomber when you could go zipping about in a speed-scout was clear out of Johnny's comprehension.

In the morning he received a letter.

"WAR DEPARTMENT
The Adjutant General's Office
Washington.

Sir:

You are hereby informed that the President of the United States has appointed you, John Powell, SECOND LIEUTENANT IN THE SIGNAL RESERVE CORPS AVIATION SECTION, to rank as such from the sixteenth day of November, one thousand nine hundred and seventeen.

By authority of the Secretary of War."

Lieutenant John Powell picked up a pen and cheerfully filled in the Oath of Office that accompanied this momentous notification.

"I, John Powell, having been appointed a Second Lieutenant in the Aviation Section of the Signal Reserve Corps, in the military

*Service of the United States do solemnly
swear (or affirm) that I will support and
defend the Constitution of the United States
against all enemies, foreign or domestic;
that I will bear true faith and allegiance to
the same; that I take this obligation freely
without any mental reservation or purpose
of evasion; and that I will well and faith-
fully discharge the duties of the office upon
which I am about to enter*: SO HELP ME
GOD."

If you had, by any chance, been sitting on
one of the green benches in front of the
colored fountain in the little park facing the
U. S. Grant Hotel in San Diego in the afternoon of Nov. 16, 1917, you might have observed a sun-and-wind-burnt flying cadet
with a white band around his campaign hat,
and crossed propellers on his sleeve, enter
a military outfitter's shop across the way.

If you were still there an hour later, you
might have seen a resplendent young officer
emerge.

You would have noted that from the slanting top of his visored cap to the polished

heels of his cordovan boots he was smartly
policed. His slender figure was encased in
a new uniform of tan whip-cord. There was
just enough flare to his breeches to set off the
slimness of his legs. Two dull gold bars
rode on his shoulder straps and a pair of
silver wings blazed on his breast. The olive
sheen of his tunic, the mahogany gloss of his
boots, his burnt skin blended so effectively
that a young lady on the steps of the hotel
was moved to exclaim: "Look, mother, quick
—there goes one—an aviator—isn't he
snappy?"

Johnny Powell had won his wings.

From San Diego, Lieutenant Powell was
shipped to Payne Field at West Point, Mis-
sissippi, an advanced school for pursuit
pilots where he was taught formation flying, the newest wrinkle in aerial warfare.

At Carlstrom Field in Arcadia, Florida,
he learned the swift and delicate ways of
the single-seater speed-scout. From Carl-
strom he graduated to the aerial gunnery

school at Dorr Field, sister field to Carl-strom.

There, in a Thomas Morse scout with a fixed Marlin machine gun, he shot at falling parachutes, at sleeve tow-targets, at moving shadows in the water and at white lime silhouettes on the ground.

It was shooting, shooting, shooting, every day, with small arms, with shot guns at soaring clay pigeons, with machine guns on rocking nacelles at moving and disappearing targets. It is one thing to stand still and shoot at a fixed mark. It is another to stand still and shoot at a moving mark. It is a third to be moving yourself and to shoot at a moving target. Now add to that the fact that your target is shooting at you. Success under those conditions constitutes real marksmanship. Pursuit pilots operated under those conditions.

In Johnny's ears was the ceaseless explosion of gun fire; the bitter smell of smokeless powder was always in his nose; his hands knew little except the trigger and the throttle and the joy-stick.

Straight shooting became as natural to him as flying, and flying, after three hundred hours in the air, in wind and rain and fog, was as natural as breathing. There was nothing that any pilot could do with an airplane in the early part of 1918 that Johnny Powell could not do, from gliding on his back, to landing in a cross-wind. He could set his plane down on a dime.

By one of these strange quirks of army administration David Armstrong's name appeared on practically every military order that Powell's did. Armstrong, to the surprise of most, had qualified for Pursuit at Rockwell Field. From then on he had travelled from field to field in Powell's wake, a self-contained, unobtrusive figure.

They had begun calling him Powell's shadow long before the two ever struck the Front. They appeared inseparable; it was one of those double-sealed friendships that had begun with a mutual enmity.

Of all the engines of war that the Government dispatched to France in 1918, one of the mightiest, perhaps, was Lieutenant John

Powell. The tow-headed pursuit pilot from the State of Washington had more capacity for destruction in his slender frame than a Livens Drum loaded with phosgene.

Late in February, trained to the minute, air-wise and eager, he was ordered to Hoboken and shipped aboard the *Bellerophon* as a casual. There were six other American-trained fliers on board, two bombing pilots, one *Corps d'armée* man and Armstrong.

At Brest, Powell and Armstrong were ordered to report to Issoudun, the American flying field below Paris. At Issoudun, Johnny was put on the newest French Nieuports under battle-wise French moniteurs and had the final touches put to his combat training.

From Issoudun sometimes you could hear the faint booming of long-range guns.

"I guess we're getting close to it now," muttered Wanninger, a sleek-haired boy from Chicago.

"All set, boy?"

"Not me," said Wanninger. "What chance have we got against pilots that have been flying three years at the front? It's suicide to get into the air with them at all.''

Late that afternoon Wanninger cracked up a ship and got transferred into the ferry service.

"What's the ferry service?" Johnny inquired innocently when he heard about it.

"Ferrying new ships up to the Front. That boy hasn't got anything to worry about now. He's wise all right.''

After a final round of practise at the aerial gunnery school at Cazeau, Lieutenant Powell was attached to the 39th Aero Squadron of the First Pursuit Group and ordered to report to the aerodrome at Toul.

The 39th, one of the first American fighting squadrons to be sent to the front, was composed entirely of American pilots and had moved into an aerodrome recently occupied by the French. It lay a short distance behind Toul, an important railway connection and the object of frequent bombing raids by the enemy. The 'drome itself was a scant fifteen miles behind the lines. The highway that ran from Toul through Nancy to Luneville was within easy shelling distance of the Hun gunners. From the field you could see in good visibility the line of observation balloons stretched along the Front.

The First Pursuit Group operated in the sector between the Meuse and the Moselle—along that portion of the front which extended from St. Mihiel to Pont-a'-Mousson.

North of the aerodrome lay Verdun with its underground army of seventy thousand men. Two daylight bombing groups and an enemy fighting squadron nested in and about the hilltops of Metz which lay some twenty miles north of Pont-a'-Mousson. A famous group of German airmen was quartered in an aerodrome at Thiaucourt just across the lines from Toul.

In short, the area to which Lieutenant Powell was ordered was bristling with activity and swarming with hostile airplanes.

"If I were you," one of the other pilots told Johnny the day he arrived, "I'd keep out of combat for a month anyway. At least I wouldn't do any attacking. You might hook with an old hand your first time out,

and I wouldn't give a nickel for your
chances. He'd knock you down in ten seconds.

"Take it easy for awhile. Get used to
your machine and your guns and Archie fire.
The first two weeks are the risky ones. If
you get past those we might see you around
for awhile."

"How much do we fly?" inquired Johnny.

"A couple of patrols a day. Two hours
apiece."

"How about voluntary patrols?"

The other laughed. "You can get out as
often as you like but you'll damn soon find
out that four hours a day in the air is
aplenty."

Johnny, unimpressed, strolled over to the
hangar to see his ship. He'd only be on the
ground every day, he figured, long enough
to get his gas tank refilled.

"Hello, Lieutenant!" a cheery voice
greeted him as he entered the gloom of the
besseneau. A mechanic with an oil-smudged
face got down from a step beside a motor

and held out a dirt-ingrained hand. It was
Herman Schwimpf.

"Well I'll be—! Well can—! Well
for——!"

The two stood beaming at each other.

"Knew you were coming," said Herman.
"Saw your name on the orders."

"How long you been here?"

"A month. Say this is a great bunch.
Want to see your ship?"

Johnny found that he had inherited an
old Nieuport, discolored with oil and smoke.
Little patches on the wing fabric concealed
the scars of former battles.

"Not much for looks," said Herman.
"The oldest pilots get the newest ships. But
this one'll be all right. We just put in a new
motor."

Johnny observed for the first time, a
shooting star with a flaming tail painted on
the fuselage. Behind was the Roman numeral I. Herman was watching him anxiously.

"Thought you'd want an insignia," he

said hopefully. "Most of the boys have
got one of their own." Further along the
line Johnny could see, beside the Eagle-and-
Dachshund squadron-insignia painted on all
the ships, such personal devices as an Ace of
Spades, a Four Leaf Clover, a Red Triangle,
a Smiling Crocodile, a Skull and Cross
Bones. Well, his would be the *Shooting
Star* again.

"O.K.," he agreed, "but what's the idea
of the One?"

"Well," explained Herman, "I figgered
you'd wear out ships pretty fast up here and
I called this the *Shooting Star First*."
Johnny was to see the numeral VI on his
ship before he was through.

"Where's Armstrong?" Herman asked.

"They held him over for another week at
Cazeau. I expect he'll be along later."

They stood talking for some time in the
dim half-light of the hangar while Johnny
soaked up information about the field, the
pilots, the ships, the sector.

"That's him!" Herman told the other
mechanics exultingly when Johnny left.

"That's the boy I been tellin' you about. If he don't bust things wide open up here I'm crazy. Hell, they practically ruled him off the streets of my home town the way he drove a car. He went through ground school like grease through a goose. And he stood 'em on their heads at San Diego.

"Wild! Say, they'll never tame that kid. He flew on his back down the main stem of Coronado and cut vertical banks around the steeple of the Methodist Church. He flew for half an hour with his head in a sack just to prove that he had the feel of the ship. Why, say, that boy put his wheels down on top of the Panama Limited running from Memphis to New Orleans. If he can shoot like he can fly he'll be running up a score in no time. Just wait, boy, just wait!"

At six o'clock of a cool, misty morning in May, Johnny Powell was one of the little knot of pilots standing outside the hangars listening to final instructions from the patrol leader. Five ships, white and ghostly in the mist, stood on the dead-line. Mechanics

were warming up the motors while the armorers loaded the feed-belts of the machine
guns.

"We will assemble directly over the field
at two thousand meters," said Captain
Worthington. "When you see me head out
North, fall in behind. Stick close and keep
formation."

"Powell?" he turned to the pilot who was
going out on his first dawn patrol. "You're
number five. Watch the land-marks going
out. If you get separated or lost, high-tail
it for home. Compass southwest. Get
everything straight?"

"Yes, sir."

Powell buttoned himself into his combination suit, buckled up the strap of his helmet and snapped on his goggles. Sergeant
Schwimpf, satisfied with the sound of the
motor climbed out of the seat of the *Shooting Star* to let Johnny in.

"Go to it, Lootenant!" he yelled in
Johnny's ear. "Go to it!"

Worthington taxied out onto the field and
headed into the wind. The motors all along

the line roared up as the ships wheeled around. Herman pulled out the wheel-chocks from Johnny's ship.

For a moment the entire formation stood poised in mid-field, like arrows ready to be loosed from the string. Worthington held up his hand. All set? Hands shot up from each of the planes. All set!

They were off the ground. One by one they broke through the low cloud ceiling and into the dazzling sunlight above. And one by one they fell into position behind Captain Worthington whose plane was identified by tiny streamers from the tail and wing-tips. Powell's ship was the last in line on the right side of the V. He soon discovered, despite Herman's confidence, that his Nieuport was not so fast as the others—at least it wasn't so fast a climber. He put on full power but still he found himself falling behind. Worthington evidently sensed his trouble because he throttled down occasionally to permit him to catch up with the flock.

From a height of two miles and through a rift in the clouds Johnny caught his first glimpse of the lines. Dawn had not yet broken over the earth below and the flashing of guns behind the lines resembled the blazing edge of a prairie fire. Not a sound came up to him.

When the clouds raveled out he could see No Man's Land, a broad "strip of murdered nature" between the fair and rolling hills of France. Not a green or living thing was visible in that pock-marked desolation, only trench works and shell holes.

WONK! WONK! WONK!

Three eight-pound shrapnel shells burst into clouds of coal-black smoke just under and behind Johnny's tail. The alert German anti-craft battery at Suippes had picked up the patrol. The *Shooting Star* stood on its nose for a moment and kicked about like a skiff on an unruly sea.

"Waco," said Johnny as he righted his ship and looked back to see if his tail was wrecked. It was his baptism of Archie fire and the concussion of the shells so close to him nearly startled him out of his pants.

He knew that Archie fire was treated as a great joke by veteran pilots; that Archie almost never brought down a plane, but these shells were breaking entirely too close. Why if that last one had been a little nearer. . . .

WONK! WONK! WONK!

Unconsciously he began to follow the manœuvres of Worthington who was pursuing an irregular course to spoil the Hun marksmanship. Below them and off to the right Johnny saw a flight of French Spads winging their way unconcernedly in Germany.

Over Pont-a'-Mousson, the extreme right boundary of the patrol, Worthington wheeled left and started back over the course. Johnny had been so busy trying to keep formation that he hadn't had much time to look about.

The very first intimation of danger that he had was when he noticed the pilot in front of him waggling his flippers violently and pointing off to the East. Then he saw that all the pilots were signalling back and forth to each other. Searching the skies to the east Johnny saw a tiny formation rising out of Germany. Swift and menacing and black against the sun they were rapidly approaching the altitude of the Nieuports.

Johnny could not know what was going on in Worthington's mind, but the patrol leader was thinking hard about Johnny at that moment. From the shape of their wings he knew the Hun squadron to be composed of Fokkers. There were five of them; they had evidently spotted the American patrol and were seeking superior altitude from which to attack, at the same time trying to keep hidden in the sun.

From the standpoint of air strategy there were but two courses open to Worthington. To attack immediately, while he had the advantage of height or to turn back inside his own lines and avoid combat. With a new and untried pilot at No. 5 he hesitated to plunge into a dog-fight. The novice would undoubtedly get separated and picked off. A tough break for a man on his first trip out.

Worthington held to his course. As the

two squadrons approached each other, Johnny Powell's heart gave a queer leap as he saw, for the first time in the air, the Black Cross of the Imperial Air Force on the wings of the Fokkers.

"Waco!"

But as they drew ever closer, still holding his altitude, Worthington saw something that filled him with alarm not only for the safety of his No. 5 but for the safety of his entire patrol.

The bobbing, dancing noses of the Fokkers were painted a brilliant red! Talk about a tough break. Here was a school of the most dangerous fighters at the front. Here was a group of brilliant pilots, victors of many an air duel. Here was a patrol from the most famous Jagdstaffel unit in Germany, *The Richthofen Circus.*

PART III

"DRINK YOUR DRINK, BABY"

PART III

"DRINK YOUR DRINK, BABY"

TUT-TUT-TUT-TUT-TUT." The other
pilots in the patrol knew that Worthington was going to attack when they heard
him fire a preliminary burst (into Germany)
to clear his guns.

They were all set, therefore, when he gave
the signal, a brisk little rocking of his ship.
What that motion actually said was this:

"We're going to close with 'em, boys.
Pick your man and follow me."

At the exact moment when the Fokkers
flashed past, to the right and a little below,
Worthington zoomed up his ship, executed a
reversement and shot down like a rocket
upon the tail of the enemy patrol leader.

Numbers two, three and four of the patrol
instantly followed his example and dived.

It was up to Powell. Without a second's hesitation he flipped over the *Shooting Star*, caught the tail-end ship of the Fokker Squadron in his ring-sights and plunged downward with his motor full on.

What had been two beautifully aligned squadrons flying in opposite directions a moment before was now a whirlpool of churning planes.

An aerial dog-fight is something to witness. The gunners of opposing Archie batteries generally lie down on their backs and survey the fracas through binoculars. The guns are quiet because a shell has an equal chance of hitting a Boche or an Allied plane.

A dog-fight is a matter of minutes—sometimes of seconds. But while it lasts there is nothing to compare with it for speed or viciousness. It may range all over the sky or revolve in a tiny area like a pin-wheel or drift a couple of miles. But it does not last long because ammunition does not last long. A pilot must, perforce, resign the contest when he runs out of cartridges. And when too many of one side have been shot down or disabled so as to make the battle unequal, the survivors must contrive a getaway.

A split-second after Johnny dived he found himself in the hottest spot of his career. Planes flashed about him on all sides. The pencil streak of tracer bullets cut the air around his plane. He was smothered in the roar of motors and the deadly crackling of machine gun fire. But he found himself on the tail of a Fokker and he hung on.

Round and round and round they went, banking steeply, like two men doing cart-wheels chasing each other. Johnny knew he had caught a Tartar the minute he began the combat; the Fokker pilot banked so swiftly and manœuvred so adroitly that Johnny couldn't hold his sights on him for a moment.

He was in the exact situation of the man who had the bear by the tail. The minute Johnny let go, he knew, the pilot would turn on him and then it would be up to Johnny to run for it. So he held his altitude and hung on like grim death, striving desperately to sight his guns.

Other battles, equally desperate were going on all around him. A blazing plane hurtled past him leaving a long broad ribbon of oily black smoke in its wake. He did not know then whether it was Hun or American but he learned later that it was a victim of Worthington's guns.

Twenty yards ahead of him two planes hooked wings and went spinning out of his sight. Their wing tips had seemed barely to touch but they whipped into each other and plunged to the earth locked in a last embrace.

Whether he suddenly discovered his squadron outnumbered or became disgusted at his inability to shake Johnny off his tail or simply decided to resign the combat, Johnny's Hun stuck down his nose and began streaking for Hunland.

Instantly Johnny nosed over and lit out after him. He dived with his throttle wide open. He felt sure that the wings of the old Nieuport must fold back, but he set his teeth and kept on down though the taut struts and the tortured wires screamed in his ears. He was gaining upon the Fokker every instant.

At seventy yards he got him dead in his sights. His fingers tightened on the triggers. He saw his tracer bullets streaking into the tail fabric of the Fokker. Very carefully he raised the nose of his ship. Like water from the nozzle of a garden hose he saw his bullets creep up and stream into the cockpit.

"Tut-tut-tut-tut-tut!" The rattle of machine gun fire broke out just behind him and tracer bullets went streaking past his ear.

"Waco!"

In holding a steady course upon the tail of his enemy he had offered himself as a target. Turning his head around he found two Hun machines on his tail and not more than forty yards away.

The next instant his propeller blade broke into bits as if it had exploded. A bullet had struck it squarely and shattered it.

Johnny stuck his nose straight down and went into a vertical dive. Far below him, spinning lazily as if there were no longer a hand on its controls, he could see the first Fokker.

"Well I got one of the Heinies anyway," he told himself. And if those two devils behind him were going to get him they'd have to travel because he was going for the earth hell-bent-for-leather.

The great fault in this scheme was the fact that Johnny was going to come down on the wrong side of the lines. The dog-fight, unbeknownst to him, had drifted with the wind that invariably blew into Germany. With his propeller gone, nothing but a long flat glide could have carried him inside his own lines.

But to straighten out meant to present himself as an excellent shot to the Huns on his tail, so he could only dive and dodge. He knew he was in trouble when he came down close enough to recognize the peculiar glint and shape of the German coal-skuttle helmets. Five hundred yards across he could see the zig-zag lines of allied trench-works. If he could carry the intervening space!

Ten feet over the Hun lines he levelled out and shot out into the torn waste between the lines. Half-way across, the *Shooting Star* began to settle. Johnny called upon every last ounce of his craftsmanship to nurse her along, but it was no good once he had lost flying speed. His wheels caught the far side of a shell-hole; the old Nieuport dug her nose into the earth and he somersaulted over and over.

Johnny found himself hanging from his safety belt upside down with his head but a few inches from the earth. The flesh of his lips was wedged between his front teeth where his mouth had struck against the cowling.

Dazed and a little bewildered, he undid his belt, dropped to the ground and crawled out from beneath the wrecked plane. His mind automatically obeyed the instructions that had been planted there during the long careful months of his training:

"Set fire to your ship to prevent it falling into the hands of the enemy."

He fumbled in the pockets of his combina-

tion to find a match to touch to the stream
trickling from the broken gasoline-feed line.

A shower of dirt from a shell awoke him
to an immediate consciousness of his position. He was down in No Man's Land and
he was being fired on! Instantly he abandoned the idea of burning his ship. No one
could get to it out there and it couldn't last
long anyway. He put his head down and
streaked it for his own lines. A second later
a shell, perfectly aimed, struck the *Shooting
Star* and blew it to hell.

A shell-hole opened a welcome mouth and
Johnny dived into it head first. Immediately
all hell broke loose around it. The two Hun
pilots, seeing their quarry on his way to
escape swooped down and poured a fusillade
into it. The entire war, for several minutes
seemed localized at this point.

"God's teeth! What the 'ell are you doing in 'ere!"

A little shrimp of a soldier in British uniform curled up under the lip of the crater
was glaring with impotent hostility at the
trespasser. The ear phones over his head

told Johnny he had stumbled into, and exposed an advanced British listening post.

"Four hours it took me to crawl out 'ere lawst night and now look what you done!"

"This your hole?" inquired Johnny not knowing a great deal about priority in such matters.

"Yes, and a hell of a mess you've made of it too."

"Want me to go?"

"You bloody kite-fliers would last a hell of a while out here you would," said the other contemptuously. He cocked his head on one side. "Hear that?"

Far off down the valley somewhere Johnny heard the sound of a horn.

"Gas. That's what it is. The gas alarm. And you ain't got no gas mask. Sure, I know that gas is a longways off but it'll be here soon enough. You can take your choice. Chance the gas and crawl back tonight—or run for it now."

Johnny took off his Teddy Bear suit; it was no outfit for a sprinter.

"Good luck," said the Tommy.

Johnny waited for a lull in the firing. When it came he catapulted himself out of the hole and lit out in a dodging, swerving sprint like a shifty quarterback in a broken field. He clipped off a good sixty yards before he dove into another hole. It was a fresh one, still hot and curling with the smoke of high explosive powder.

He had seen heads popping up from the British trenches and heard the sharp zip of rifle fire and he knew that they were covering his retreat—picking off the Germans who were sniping at him. Good old Tommies!

In a series of skip-stops Johnny made his way right up to the British wire. Flat on his stomach he wriggled back and forth along the wire trying to find an opening to let him through.

In the end a big sergeant came warily over the top of the trench ambled out on his hands and knees and led Johnny back through. They gave him a cheery reception when he rolled over the face of the parapet.

"Jolly well run, Leftenant!"

"Good effort, sir."

"A good job you didn't try to crash the wire."

A British intelligence officer came up and asked Johnny for information on the terrain, activities and aspect of operations beyond the lines.

All that Johnny could think of was that he had seen a hell of a lot of dead Germans out there, a statement that seemed to please the Major no end. He took Johnny to the dressing station to have his lips treated and then invited him over to Brigade headquarters to have a spot of Scotch.

From there Johnny telephoned to the field to report that he was O.K. and they told him to stand by that they would send a car over for him.

A balloon observer had already telephoned the news of Johnny's victory into the airdrome before he arrived.

"What did I tell you!" cried Herman, triumphantly, "What did I tell you!"

The older pilots congratulated Johnny, but they told each other privately that the kid would not last long. He had used up all his luck in his first ride. The novice pilot had got one of the Richthofen Circus and had escaped from a crash in No Man's Land. He was the product of two miracles already and no airman was entitled to more than one in the same day. He was another of those morning glories that bloomed along the front.

His feat, however, served to draw immediate attention to him, attention that he did not lose during his period of service with the 39th Pursuit.

Very early he endeared himself to his brother pilots by his eagerness for fighting.

No sooner did he land from a two-hour patrol than he filled up his tank and set off on lone Hun-hunting excursions of his own when he could get permission.

But his natural antipathy to discipline had already asserted itself and he had been twice reprimanded for deserting his patrol. Only the fact that his courage was above suspicion saved him from a court martial.

Evidently bored with flying a straight course in formation up and down the lines, he had suddenly broken off and gone cruising about in Hunland on his own, looking for a fight.

His patrol leader had reported it to the Commanding Officer, and Johnny was put on the carpet.

The next time he left his patrol he took good care to bring down a plane before he came back. It was an unwary photographic ship behind Rheims, and he shot it down in full view of a French Archie battery who reported it back to his airdrome.

Johnny discovered then that the way to stave off a reprimand was to perform a deed which called for commendation. Every plane he shot down added to the score and prestige of the 39th Pursuit, and he could see that the C.O. was hard put to it to commend and censure a pilot at the same time.

Up until the time Armstrong joined the Squadron, Johnny had been a lone wolf. With Armstrong's coming there sprung up one of those curious combinations which occasionally occurred between fliers at the Front: a team. Armstrong attached himself to Johnny and the two invariably flew off together. There were several such teams on the Front: Guynemer and Raymond, Luke and Werner, Billy Wellman and Tommy Hitchcock.

The pilots in the 39th didn't take readily to David. They didn't get him at all. His reserve amounted to taciturnity. He made friends with no one. His reports were models of terseness. He seemed to have but one passion and that was his idolatry for Johnny Powell.

He was rarely more than twenty feet behind Johnny at any time. There was something uncanny in the relationship in that neither, either by word or gesture, ever betrayed his feeling for the other. Whatever bond it was that held them together was below the surface.

In Armstrong's eyes there was something of the haunted look of a condemned man. He knew—for he had seen—that Johnny Powell carried Sylvia's miniature case

A Paramount Picture. Wings.

"SPEED" POWELL PAYS A BRIEF CALL ON THE TRENCHES IN THE HEAT OF
THE ST. MIHIEL FRAY.

A Paramount Picture. *Wings*
AIRPLANES SPRINGING FROM HIDDEN HANGARS PROTECT THE YANKEE ADVANCE.

about his neck on the cord with his identification tags. He knew also what was written on the back of Sylvia's picture. And knowing Johnny's intensity he foresaw what would happen when Johnny discovered the truth.

It was as if Johnny carried a case of dynamite beneath his chin. Some day, somewhere it would explode and David knew that the explosion would smash their friendship to a thousand atoms. Yet there was no way by which he could fend it off. He could only live in dread of the hour. The dread was reflected in his eyes.

They were sitting in the Alerte Tent one morning, early in June when an orderly brought over the mail.

"Lieutenant Armstrong?"

Johnny reached up to pass the letters over to his friend. But David caught his arm and took the letters himself. It was a quick, almost rude gesture. Johnny looked at him curiously. Queer fellow, David. Did queer things.

The letters, of course, were from Sylvia,

a half a dozen of them. Johnny could not
have failed to recognize the hand-writing.
Johnny received but one or two treasured
letters a month from Sylvia.

The talk amongst the pilots on the Alerte
was usually of Paris, femmes, the Rue la
Bray, the Chatham bar, new ships, and
motors. But mostly of femmes.

"Gosh, what a quick come-back," Cliff
Chapman said, "she had on an emerald
bracelet, one of those new jointed ones, and I
said what did that cost you, baby, and she
said, quick as a flash:

" '*Cinq minutes de folie.*' "

To Johnny, the free talk of women was a
little startling. After all he was still the
tow-headed boy from Temple, Washington,
and he had only just come to France.

As mad as he was in the air, he had not
yet arrived at the attitude on the ground
of the war fliers.

They were all members of the legion of
the living dead. A pursuit pilot at the front
figured himself a dead man. And many of
them lived, loved and drank as dead men.

The next ride was always the last. Each trip to Paris was the final one. Each kiss was a never-to-be-repeated farewell to life.

They had all gone, the Boelckes, the Balls, the Guynemers, the Immelmans, the best among them. It was your turn next.

If Johnny didn't yet share this fatalism the talk at least awakened in him a sharp curiosity to see Paris and perhaps to taste a little of life before he was killed. Of course he wouldn't go with any French girls because, well, because of Sylvia. After all he intended to keep himself for her.

Armstrong handed a copy of the Temple *Vidette* containing an account—exaggerated from an A. P. dispatch—of Lt. Powell's first air victory in France.

Johnny regarded it indifferently.

"You don't care so much for them, back home," remarked David.

Johnny shook his head.

"Nope," and then as an afterthought, "except for one—or two."

A troubled look crept into Armstrong's eyes and he fell silent.

"How do you get to go to Paris?" Johnny inquired of Chapman.

"Knock down a few Huns and get a leave and, boy, you better get there quick because pretty soon it'll be too late."

They were arguing the various merits of the French women when the signal came, through the little field telephone in the Alerte Tent. A Gotha was reported heading west over Bar-le-Duc attended by two escort planes.

Johnny got to the *Shooting Star* in a side-car first. The dust of his take-off was still hanging in the air when Armstrong got away. Holabird got off but motor trouble forced him back to the field.

Bar-le-Duc had suffered much from day and night bombing raids. When the towns-folk heard the distant drone of the big, bi-motored plane they ducked for the cellar-ways.

Wham! Wham! Wham! Wham!

The bombs, released at fifth-second intervals, struck the village in shattering percussions. Overhead the Gotha, like a giant vulture, wheeled and turned.

Wham! Wham! Wham! Wham! Wham!

The Gotha had proceeded on its second flight over the village when a dark shadow flashed across the powdery white street. Then came a short burst of machine gun fire and two or three figures emerged cautiously from shelter and gazed into the sky. A single plane, tiny and direct as a wasp, was winging its way for the Gotha. Behind it, streaking along the sky came a second. The Gotha pilot, seeing his danger, tripped his triggers and released the last of his bombs from the bomb rack. They fell harmlessly in a field at the north end of town.

The people came swarming into the streets to watch the fight; there was little danger now except from a stray spattering of machine gun bullets.

The first of the oncoming planes, as if unaware of the presence of the two escort ships poised above, made straight for a position above the Gotha and half-circled for an attack.

Down they came, the two protection ships, side by side. And as they dropped out of the sky another plane hurled itself at them from the side. Armstrong engaged them both while Powell swooped down upon the Gotha.

The Gotha, however big and slow to respond to controls, was no defenseless prey for a chasse pilot. It carried besides a pilot and navigator, two gunners, one in the nose, and one in the rear cockpit. A third gun unbeknownst to Johnny operated through a tunnel in the floor of the fuselage.

From the standpoint of the villagers the fight was a peach. They saw the little Nieuport darting about the big bomber like a sparrow-hawk after a crow.

Johnny's first dive carried him past the tail of the ship to a choice position under its body. At least he figured it a choice position until he pulled up the nose of his Nieuport to pour a stream into its underpart and found the third gun blazing away in his face. Bullets ripped holes in the wing fabric of the *Shooting Star II* but luckily did not find either the motor, the gas tank or the pilot.

"Waco!" said Johnny and swerved out from under instantly.

"So that's how it is . . . shooting through the floor, hey . . . well that's different." Johnny regained his position above and behind the Gotha and took new count of his enemy. "Well, I don't see how the hell . . . I'm going to smack you down . . . unless I shoot it out with you. . . ."

The Gotha was protected at every vulnerable point, nose, tail and underpart. "No blind spot . . . boy, you sure looked funny popping up and down between those two guns . . . like a jack-in-the-box . . . well, old jack-in-the-box . . . here's your chance. . . ." Both Hun gunners were following the Nieuport with their guns as it circled warily, above. "Coming at you, big boy." Johnny whipped over his ship and shot down on the Gotha in a swift, perpendicular dive. "Here we go . . . here we go. . . ."

Whether the suddenness of the attack dis-

concerted him or the manœuvring of the
pilot spoilt his aim or his guns jammed,
Johnny never knew, but one of the three cost
the rear gunner his life for one of Johnny's
bullets found his neck and he toppled over
on the scarf-mount, his body half hanging
out of the ship.

"Got *him* . . . can you beat that!" It
was pure luck getting that observer. "He
should have potted me . . . just shot in the
pants with luck that's me . . . that's kid
Powell . . . just shot in the pants—oh, you
would, would you—you'd run away now,
would you—" With his rear gunner out and
his tail exposed to attack, the pilot of the
Gotha put down his nose and turned into
Germany. One of the escort planes had
fallen to Armstrong's guns and the other
was trailing across the sky with Armstrong
in pursuit.

"Wait a minute there, big fella . . . if
these here guns don't jam. . . . I've got a
little present for you . . . how would you
like to go down and pick a four-leaf clover
. . . you know better than to try to run

away . . . you aren't fast enough . . . you ought to stick around and fight it out."

Diving from a beautiful position above and behind, Johnny held his fire until he was less than forty yards off. The outline of the giant Gotha completely filled his ring sights when he pressed his trigger. His tracer bullets crept along the tail of the ship and poured into the cockpit. . . .

A demonstration broke out amongst the spectators below when they saw the great bomber suddenly soar up like a wounded bird and fall off on a wing. A bullet had reached the pilot. Spinning lazily the Gotha fell in a beet field just off the main highway to the north of Bar-le-duc.

Within a quarter of an hour the wreck was surrounded by a milling throng of villagers and soldiers, and five minutes later it lay as bare as the bleached skeleton of a horse. Eager souvenir-hunting hands stripped it of its instruments and fittings. Hardly a patch of fabric remained.

Johnny Powell did not go back to his field for two days. Instead, he landed at a

French airdrome, where he was received joyously. The French pilots liked him because, as they said, he was just a little *touché,* and, as they very well knew, the best chasse pilots were always a little mad.

Stories of the Temple flier had already trickled into the airdromes along the Western front; anything might be expected of the wild egg from the 39th. Major Brand, Johnny's C. O., did not report him missing because he suspected that he was hiding out somewhere. Anyway there had been a mysterious telephone call into the Squadron Headquarters asking about Armstrong, was he safe? Had he come back after the fight? On being told, the caller hung up without explanation. The Major had figured that that was Powell asking about his team-mate.

"Damn that boy," said the Major. "I'm going to recommend him for the Croix de Guerre first and court-martial him afterwards."

But he carried out only the first half of his threat for Johnny further distinguished himself on his way home.

In the half-light of the early dawn a Nieu-port appeared suddenly out of the mist and speared a German drachen with incendiary bullets just as the balloon crew were unreel-ing it behind Thiaucourt. The red glow lit up the sky for miles around and there were a half dozen confirmations of the feat on hand when Powell turned in his report.

The Major found it difficult to reprimand a pilot who had, in two days, destroyed many thousand dollars worth of enemy property. He started in by giving him hell and ended by ordering him to report for the decoration ceremony the following Tuesday.

"Order de L'Armée:

Le Lieutenant John Powell Pilote de chasse plein d'audace et d'un sang-froid extraordinaire joignant de brillantes quali-tés de pilotage avec courage. Le 28 Juillet à la suite d'un dur combat a abattu un Gotha ennemi."

But the most interesting part of the cita-tion to Johnny, standing ankle-deep in the thick gumbo of the field during a slanting rain with Dave and a handful of others, be-

fore a one-armed French General, was the
rider attached. It granted him a six-day
leave in Paris—the most precious gift that
the commanding officer could bestow upon a
pilot.

"Paris! W-a-c-o, brothers!"

"Going to step out amongst 'em, eh,
boy?"

"Take 'er low and slow, Lieutenant."

"Keep out of a tail-spin, son."

The fliers volunteered much sage advice
the morning Johnny and Dave drove off
down the highway toward Paris in the big
tan Cadillac.

By ten o'clock that night Johnny and
David had seen a good cross-section of war-
time Paris. At Henri's Bar, the first stop,
they had hooked up with Timberlake and St.
Ives, two other pilots from the 39th Pursuit.
St. Ives was an albino midget. Pat Timberlake was a handsome, big-handed flier with
three Huns to his credit.

"We'll go up on the hill," explained Timberlake, who'd been in Paris before, "but
first we got to get organized."

So they spent the first part of the evening in getting organized. They got organized at Henri's, at Ciro's, at Claridge's, at Maxim's. At the Crillon Bar they saw a huge Australian, fresh from the front, order twenty brandies to be set up in single glasses in a sparkling row along the polished surface of the bar. He sat up on one of the high stools and began to toss them off one after another. He drank his way successfully to the eleventh before he fell off and five men carried him out.

"Well," said Timberlake after they were pretty well organized, "let's step out amongst 'em. What do you say, soldiers?"

"O.K." they agreed.

"And I know where they prowl," he added. "The Folies Bergère," he told the driver when they clambered in a fiacre outside the Crillon.

"That's where they prowl," he said, "and boy you better hold onto your hat," he said turning to Johnny, "because they'll go for you."

"Sure they will," agreed Jimmy St. Ives,

"that pink and white complexion, those baby blue eyes and that angelic expression . . . they'll eat him up."

"Not me," said Johnny firmly. He was thinking of Sylvia.

"Get promenoirs," Timberlake told St. Ives when they disembarked in front of the theater. "You don't want to sit. Waste of time sitting down, watching a show when there's so much plain and fancy drinking to be done."

So they got four promenoirs and entered the great hall of the Folies Bergère. The place was packed, jammed, thronged with military. They milled about the fountain, the orchestra stand in the center, the tables, they swarmed up and down the curling staircase at the far end of the hall, they circled about the railed gallery above.

It was a vivid intermingling of allied soldiery, in horizon blue, in scarlet, in buff, in madder-red, in gosling green, in khaki. And each with a girl on his arm. The place was ablaze with color, alive with sound, heavy with scent. Warriors' night out.

All that Johnny saw of the show at the Folies Bergère that night was a glimpse from the promenade of six half-nude women on a spread fan, the *défile de zouaves, de spahis, de trompettes* and *de tambours,* and a young lady who sang something about:

"J'ai des p'tits pois un peu partout...."

For Timberlake and St. Ives never did succeed in getting past the Bar Américain in the corner. It had been a long ride up from the Crillon, they pointed out, and they had to get organized again.

They got down off their stools every once in a while to take a tour about the fountain just to see that everything was under control, but they always made their way back, like homing pigeons, to the crowd three-deep about the bar.

Johnny didn't mind much because it was very exciting just cruising about the lounge with Dave. It was exciting sitting on one of the red-and-white wicker chairs at one of the funny little round-topped, wire-legged tables in the center just off the aisle with the crowd passing at your elbow.

Every girl that passed left a cloud of perfume in her wake. The smell of jasmine and rose and violet and chypre was very thrilling to nostrils that were accustomed to the odor of petrol and burnt castor oil and smokeless powder. It made him light-headed. Besides, there was a provocative, bitter-sweet, salty scent that came from the girls themselves.

"Got your safety belt buckled?" Timberlake and St. Ives, who said that they were organized now, came over and joined them.

Johnny had never seen such girls. Starry-eyed, crimson-lipped little devils in black-glove-silk dresses.

"*Souvenir!*" A hand reached down, seized the bronze-and-silver crossed-wing-and-propeller insignia on Johnny's collar and tore it loose.

"Hey!" He seized her wrist.

"*Souvenir! Souvenir!*"

Johnny looked helplessly at Timberlake. "What's this souvenir business?"

"She wants something to remember you by—when *la guerre est finie.*"

A Paramount Picture.

BRUCE IS SHOT DOWN BEHIND THE ENEMY'S LINES.

Wings.

She was a shapely little blonde with tiny white teeth and a bee-stung lower lip.

Johnny looked up into her face.

"Allô, bébé," she said, "buy me a drink."

"You better take her to sit down," said Timberlake, "or you'll have her in your lap."

"Prenez-place," said St. Ives.

"I told you they'd go for him," Timberlake said. "We'll be flooded with tarts in a minute."

"Qu'il est beau!" said Christine, looking at Johnny, *"l'aviateur Americain."*

"He doesn't drink enough," St. Ives explained. "He ought to drink more."

"He is not long to live, eh? He should amuse himself."

Christine flung her arms around Johnny's neck and gave him a playful nip on the ear. The blood ran down his neck and over the collar of his blouse.

"You don't like little Christine?" she cried. "No?"

Johnny wiped his ear with his handkerchief and said she mustn't do that again.

"Do you know what?" said Timberlake looking at a tall Dragoon, "I ought to have a pair of red pants. I've wanted a pair of red pants since I was a child. Now when my chance came for a pair of red pants I went and joined the wrong service. Isn't that a hell of a note?"

"What in the hell would you do in a pair of red pants?"

"Damned if I know, but I fancy myself in a pair of red pants. I wonder if I could persuade one of those frogs to change with me."

"You sit still," said St. Ives, "and drink your drink."

"*Mon petit loup-loup,*" said Christine.

"What is she saying?" Johnny inquired.

"She says you're her little wolf-wolf."

"What a mistake, I made," Timberlake mourned, "in joining a service that hasn't even got a dress uniform."

"*Souvenir.*" A hand flashed across Johnny's face and ripped one of the gold buttons from his blouse.

"We'll have to take him home in a barrel," observed St. Ives.

"If I had it to do over again," said Timberlake, "do you know what I'd join?"

St. Ives said he couldn't imagine for the life of him.

"The Sixth Inniskilling Dragoons," said Timberlake, "they've got a scarlet tunic with primrose facings and a steel helmet with a white plume."

"You'd look swell in a white plume."

"What is a *chou?*" Johnny inquired again.

"A *chou,* my boy, is a cabbage."

"And what is a *chou-fleur?*"

"A cabbage flower. It seems to me that you are progressing very rapidly, young man," said St. Ives severely. "A minute ago you were only her little wolf-wolf and now you are her little cauliflower. Take your time, son, take your time."

"*Souvenir!*" Johnny, who was sitting in the most exposed position nearest the aisle, had lost two more buttons, the bronze

"U. S." on his collar-band and one of the gold lieutenant's bars from his shoulder strap.

"You better protect your little cauliflower," St. Ives told Christine, "or pretty soon he won't have anything left but his pants buttons."

So Christine moved around and put Johnny on the inside.

"If I'd joined up with 3rd Hussars, now," said Timberlake ruminatively, "I'd have a garter-blue Busby bag."

"The Royal Fusiliers have got a red stripe down their pants and a bearskin shako."

"Don't fancy myself in a bearskin shako," objected Timberlake, "they catch fleas."

The curtain went down inside the theater and the orchestra in the lounge caught up the refrain:

"Oh, Madelon, you are the only one . . .
Oh, Madelon, for you we carry on. . . ."

"Vielle bique!" Christine was saying to Johnny.

"I never saw such a fellow," St. Ives said. "First he's a wolf and then he's a cauliflower and now he's an old goat. You ought to make up your mind, young lady," he told Christine, "if he's going to be a zoo or a truck garden."

Christine was becoming very annoyed with Johnny because he failed to respond to her endearments.

"What is the matter with your frien'?" she demanded. "W'y he don' drink? W'y he don' laugh? W'y he don' play wiz Christine?"

"He's bashful," St. Ives explained. "He's the quiet kind. Just wait till he gets started."

"W'en you goin' start, *bébé?*"

"It's so long since we have seen a miss,
Won't you give us just a kiss. . . ."

"I wish to hell I belonged to the Royal Horse Guards or the King's Own Scottish Borderers or the Black Watch or the Hussars or the Cuirassiers or the Dragoons or something," complained Timberlake.

"You drink your drink and forget the Dragoons."

"I like an outfit that's got eighteen rows

of gold braid and pipings and braidings and shoulder-cords and red tabs and hackles and jack boots and cummerbunds——"

"You certainly would knock 'em dead in a cummerbund."

"Wouldn't I, though. I like an outfit that's lousy with tradition and that's got a song and things. Hell, we haven't even got a song."

"We've got a thirst though."

"*Je suis folle de toi,*" whispered Christine.

Johnny looked inquiringly at St. Ives.

"She says you're her little woolly lamb and she'd like to be your godmother."

"A hell of an outfit, the Air Service," said Timberlake gloomily. "Just a step-child. No song, no red pants——"

"No ships."

"That's right. No ships."

"*You called me broken doll a year ago,*
  You said that I was very nice to know
      . . ."

Christine was bent on taking Johnny off somewhere. It was more exciting elsewhere.

"What did you do other places? Oh," she shrugged her shoulders, *"on y danse, on y rit."*

"Come wiz me," she begged. "Jus' be my camarade tonight."

No. No. No.

His persistent refusals aroused a storm in her eyes.

"I know w'y you don' wan' play wiz Christine," she said suddenly. "You have lit-tle sweet'eart back 'ome."

Johnny didn't know why he repudiated the suggestion immediately, but he did. Of course not! But his hands went involuntarily to the neck-band of his blouse. The movement betrayed him to Christine.

"I soon found what love was, I thought
*   I knew,*
But that has only taught me, honey,
*   how I love you."*

Christine slipped her arm about Johnny's neck and began to whisper in his ear. She slipped her finger down inside his neck-band and hooked it around the thin little silver chain of the locket.

"Zut!" she cried triumphantly and gave the chain a quick jerk. It broke and Johnny saw the locket dangling from her hand.

David, fascinated by the jiggling head of the giant negro in the yellow burnous on the balcony, had gone upstairs to attend the *danse du ventre*. Timberlake was off looking for a pair of red pants and St. Ives was receiving the attentions of a dark-eyed daughter of joy.

"Give me that!"

"Non!" Christine had it open and was gazing intently at the blonde head inside.

"Give it back!"

"Moment!"

Johnny seized her hand, pressed open her fingers and the locket fell to the floor. The catch flew apart and the stiff little miniature popped out on the floor. The message on the back lay exposed.

Johnny made a dive for the locket which had rolled underneath his chair and Christine picked up the picture. She made out the writing while Johnny groped for the locket.

When he sat up and asked her for the picture she gave it to him without a word, face up.

Johnny fitted the picture back into the case and snapped it shut.

"And then you said you'd love me in
return,
Don't tell me you were fooling after
all. . . ."

"She is ver' pretty, your sweet'eart," said Christine.

The moment, it seemed, had passed. The kindly godfather that looked after Johnny's destiny, it appeared, was protecting him. The orchestra kept on playing Broken Doll, the newest American jazz piece. The crowd continued circling about the lounge.

But a few minutes later Christine turned to him again.

"Give me a cigarette, David."

Johnny looked blankly into her face.

"David," he repeated. "My name isn't David."

"Ah, yes," said Christine. "It is so."

Johnny shook his head. "That's my

buddy's name. The boy who was sitting over there."

"W'y you don't want to tell me your name, *cheri?* It is David. I know it is David."

"Don't be funny."

"But it is so."

"Why is it so?"

"I saw."

"Saw what?"

"Saw it there. In the locket. David Ar-r-mstrong."

"Where in the locket?"

"Behind the figure. Written so."

Johnny opened the locket, pried out the picture and turned it over in his hand.

A sudden roaring burst in his ears. The earth rose and heaved beneath his chair. In a tiny clear hand on the back of the square he read:

"To David Armstrong, with heart's dearest love.

Sylvia."

"Well for——!"

Christine was holding a glass to his lips.

"Drink your drink, baby."

PART IV

THE TALISMAN

PART IV

THE TALISMAN

AT ten o'clock in the evening, Mary-Louise Preston was tooling along the Champs Élysées in her truck, headed for the Gare St. Lazare. A block or so past Claridge's she caught sight of a short, thick and familiar figure moving along the sidewalk.

Herman Schwimpf! He belonged to the 39th Aero Squadron and he could tell her where Johnny was!

She pulled up to the curb, jumped off the truck and ran after him.

"Herman!"

He turned and his face lighted up.

"Why, Mary!"

"Where's Johnny?"

"Johnny Powell? Guess he's out on a loop."

"A loop?"² A *loop*. Mary had seen fliers on a loop before and she knew what Herman meant.

"Here? In Paris?"

"Yep."

"But where is he now?"

"Don't know. I'm looking for him myself."

"Why? What for?"

"His leave's been recalled and they want him back at the field. They want all the pilots back."

Herman pulled a flimsy out of his pocket and showed it to her. Lt. Powell's name was on the list of officers ordered to report back immediately "on receipt of this order."

"Major Brand phoned the Provost Marshal to round them up and send 'em back," said Herman, "and he sent me in to try and find them. They're getting ready for the Big Push, I guess."

"Where is he staying—what hotel?"

"The Madelon. They're all staying there. But none of 'em are in now; I've got to go out and look for them."

"Let me go along."

"Sure," agreed Herman, "come along."

The fact that Johnny was wanted back at his field had stiffened Mary in the purpose already forming in her mind.

In the first place, the thought of Johnny on a loop in Paris gave her a pang of heart-sickness. Would he behave like the rest of the war fliers and let himself go? Would he drink and not respect himself?

She would find him, she must find him before the night was over.

Mary Preston's search for John Powell in Paris that night became an odyssey. She knew, better than Herman, where she might find Johnny, because she had been in and out of Paris for months and she knew where the aviators congregated. At Maxim's, Ciro's, the Chatham Bar, the Crillon and then up the hill into Montmartre.

Through the shifting crowds of Paris she moved that evening, a slender, boyish figure hurrying from uniform to uniform, peering from face to face, searching for one man.

She lost Herman early. He ran into a couple of pals who held him up for a drink, besides he was nothing like so keen and eager as Mary, and he held her back, really, though he was, in his hero-worshipping way, very much in earnest about finding Powell and Armstrong.

Mary had a pre-vision of what she was going to find when she would finally catch up with them because she crossed and recrossed their starry trails half a dozen times.

Mary had traced her way through nearly every night resort of wartime Paris when she reached the Folies. She saw that he was not at the Bar, but when she circled the promenade she saw that her search was over.

At a table in the corner just off the isle, sat Johnny Powell, Johnny Powell with a hot, desperate face and fever-bright, unseeing eyes.

His hair curled down over his forehead in damp circles. His tunic was open at the throat, his collar insignia was gone, and the front of his blouse was torn where an eager hand had snatched at his silver wings. There was no doubt that Johnny was on a loop.

He was one of a group of hilarious young officers and animated *joyeuses*. His dark, young face and gabardine uniform contrasted against the white complexions of the girls. It was the first time she had seen Johnny in a year and the sight of him awoke all her old devotion to him.

She wanted to run instantly to him but she was seized with an overpowering timidity. Suppose he didn't want to see her now? Maybe he might not even recognize her. He wasn't well, he wasn't himself.

She stood uncertainly, looking at him; one of the girls leaned over, took Johnny's face between her hands, tilted back his head and kissed him on the lips. Oh la la!

A tremor of weakness passed through Mary's body. She felt suddenly helpless. She could not summon up courage to walk over to this group. She felt awkward, out of place in her uniform, as if she had no business here.

"Vi-o-lets, who'll buy my vi-o-lets. . ."

One of the fliers, persuaded by a girl, rose from the table.

"Ready to take off?" someone said.

"All set?"

"Keep her nose on the horizon and don't skid on your turns."

Christine put her mouth to Johnny's ear. *"Viens."*

He shook his head stubbornly. There was a puzzled, bewildered look in his face, like one who has been deranged by an accident and is vainly trying to collect himself.

"Viens!"

He pushed her away.

"Gosse!" she cried.

The others at the table regarded Johnny solicitously.

"Zig-zag?"

"Il a trop bu," said Christine.

"Pauv' petit."

Mary-Louise came up timidly behind Johnny's chair.

"Johnny."

He did not turn his head.

"Johnny." She put her hand on his shoulder. "Johnny—Johnny—Johnny."

"*Qu'est-ce que vous voulez?*" demanded Christine angrily.

Intimidated, Mary fell back.

She was very near to a *crise des larmes.* She saw that Johnny must leave, sooner or later—even now the lounge was emptying —and that he would not go unaccompanied. Tears stood in her eyes. She made her way blindly along the wall to the "Dames" in the corner off the promenade.

"*Qu' est-ce que c'est, petite?*"

The old woman attendant regarded her with compassionate eyes. She was an age-less, bewhiskered creature, and she sat in her mirrored corner in front of the shelves of perfumes, cosmetics and toilet waters, which no one ever bought. Nor no one ever saw anyone else buy.

"*Qu' est-ce que c'est?*"

Instead of steadying her, the note of tenderness in her voice had the opposite effect upon Mary-Louise. She began to cry.

"*Pauvre petite.* Tell Julie."

Mary-Louise did tell Julie. She told Julie everything. She even led Julie out into the promenade and pointed out Johnny's table and Johnny.

"Zig-zag," pronounced the old lady of the lavabo.

To Julie's Gallic way of thinking, there was but one thing to do. If that was your man and you wanted him, you must go and take him. Especially if he was zig-zag. She looked dubiously at Mary's uniform. Not so attractive to a boy who was trying to forget war for a moment. Had she no dress?

The boy was girl-hungry, *n'est-ce pas,* wine-thirsty. He wanted to amuse himself, *non?* He had not so long to live. These men of the air were not so long to endure. How long? Two—three months?

Would the little one put on a costume if Julie found one? She would look very chic in a costume, the old lady said, looking at Mary's eyes and skin. Julie could obtain one from the wardrobe mistress. The wardrobe mistress was her friend, you under-

stand. She might borrow one for the night.
The little one would bring it back? She
thought of one now, a nice one, *très, très
chic,* a nice color, citron, with stockings and
slippers to match.

And she must touch some color to her
face. So pale she was, the little one. And
she must be very *gai,* she must laugh.

The presence of new arrivals at Johnny's
table meant little to him since he was
experiencing some difficulty in identi-
fying those who were already there. The
music was now faint—now loud in his ears.
The room wheeled about him every time he
closed his eyes and the string of frosted
light bulbs around the balcony undulated
up and down like a serpentine. His eyes,
like a child's, fixed themselves in strange
and absorbed wonder upon the objects
about him.

He noticed, with astonishment, the photo-
graphs of the half-clad girls on the square
pillars supporting the balcony, he focused
on the glass enclosed cabinets containing the
porcelain dolls, the bottles, the figurines.

Signs caught his eye. Cinzano . . . Celeste et Ses Chiens . . . Perriere . . . Ballet Russe . . . He! Marie! . . . Bar Americain . . . Champagne Guy Precy. . . .

When he thought of all the letters he had written to that girl. Of all the things he had said. . . .

Mistinguette . . . Vermouth, 4f . . . Harry Pilcer . . . Lido Venice . . . Eve la Celebre Danseuse Americaine . . . Gin, 3f . . . Raquel Meller . . . Le Bal Tabarin. . . .

They had made a noodle out of him. They knew he had the locket, both of them. They let him keep it. Let him go on thinking the way he did. Humoring him.

Le Celebre Jazz-band . . . Dubonnet . . . Jocelyn . . . Port Wine, 3f . . . Le Monico . . . "Drink your drink, baby". . . Le Moulin Rouge . . . Syphons, 11f. . . .

The Folies Bergère became a series of broken phrases, a dog-fight of sound and movement, a shifting pattern of faces, arms, silken legs, perfumes, a shuffling succession of blurred images.

But, ever-recurrent, came the stinging,

bitter thought of his humiliation biting into
his consciousness, like acid biting into a
copper plate. He had been made ridiculous.

"But when you go away,
You'll be sorry some day,
You left behind a broken doll."

A couple of sailors jumped into the fountain and were sporting about, giving seal-
barks and splashing water over each other.
Life on the Pribiloff Islands.

"C'est drôle, la vie," said Christine,
laughing at the sailors in the fountain.

"What's she say?"

"She says life is very funny," said the
girl in the yellow sequins at his elbow.

"That's right. Life—life is funny."

"Et triste alors."

"She says life is very funny and very
sad."

"Right. Tha's absoluly right. Life is
funny's hell. And sad. You don' know how
funny life is. You're too young-to-unner-
stan'. Say," said Johnny, looking uncertainly at the yellow sequins, "You got bubbles on your dress." The halation on the

polished little wafers made them grow and
swell in his eyes.

"Don't you know me?"

"Sure. You're Musidora or something.
And I'm David. Shake your head, you've
got bubbles in your hair."

It was funny how he hadn't noticed those
bubbles before. Why they were everywhere.
They were spouting out of the open mouth
of the champagne bottle. They were cascad-
ing over the table. The beading on the door
was a creeping line of bubbles. The rows of
electric lights were a dancing string of
bubbles.

"Nev' saw so many bubbles."

Two great tears stood for a moment in
the eyes of the girl in the yellow sequins,
and started to roll down her face.

Johnny put out his finger. "Bubbles,"
he said. "A couple of bubbles."

"Let's go," said Mary-Louise. "Please
let's go home."

"No, sir." He talked with the curious
fixity of a sleep-walker.

"Please come with me. I'm your friend."

"Don' believe in friends. Don' ever believe in frien's. They double-cross you. Shake your head. You got a lotta bubbles in your hair."

"But it's time to go."

"Where's ev'body?"

"Gone home. They've all gone home."

"Whaffor?"

"It's late. It's time to go."

"Kiss me."

"No."

"*Kiss* me."

"No."

"Why?"

"Not now."

"Who cares? Who cares if I kiss you or not? What difference does it make? You better kiss me."

"Not here."

"*Will* you kiss me?"

"Maybe."

"Where?"

"When we go."

Johnny rose uncertainly to his feet. Christine rose with him.

"If you go, *bébé,*" she said, "you go wiz Christine." Christine and Mary-Louise faced each other. Certainly Christine had prior rights to the zig-zag aviator.

Johnny said he was going with the bubble girl.

"*Non!*" cried Christine.

Johnny solved the problem very neatly for them. The bubbles suddenly burst. He wavered unsteadily for a moment, executed a half-virage, fell off into a spin and nose-dived across the table. Christine took one look at the figure face downward on the table, collected her vanity case, her cigar-ettes and her souvenirs and departed.

What it amounted to in the end was that Mary-Louise took her old playmate home and put him to bed. An attendant helped her get him to a cab and the porteur at the Madelon assisted her in getting him upstairs into his room.

Ah, the handsome young officier Ameri-cain. Too bad. Too bad. He wanted to amuse himself in the so short time. He was not long to live, eh, in the flying service? He did not know the wines of France. In the morning it would be all right again. . . . *Il dort comme un enfant.*

They arranged him on the bed. The silver locket with the broken chain slipped out of the side pocket of his blouse. Mary-Louise picked it up. Dear Johnny. Was he carrying that funny little snap-shot of her around with him.

She opened the case. For a long time she stood quite still, looking down at Sylvia's picture. She moved over to the window, opened the curtains, looked down upon the street-lights glistening in the dark wet pavements.

The rain beat gently against the tall windows. Indistinct figures passed below. It was Paris—night-time. Mary's head inclined against the glass. Maybe Johnny was right. Life was very funny and very sad. And what difference did it make and who cared?

She unhooked the collar of Johnny's blouse so that he might breathe more easily, she kissed his hot forehead, picked up the little bundle that contained her uniform and things and left. Good bye, Johnny boy.

"Snap into it there, Ace of Aces. . . . !"

"Come to life, Lieutenant! Your country calls you, in her hour of peril."

Timberlake, Jimmie St. Ives and Armstrong were in the room, fully dressed.

Armstrong emptied the water carafe over Johnny's head. Johnny returned to a blurry consciousness of the fliers in the room and the sunlight streaming in the windows.

They were all looking down at him and laughing at him. Laughing to find him still with his clothes on and towels wrapped around his boots. They had not been able to draw his boots off, Mary and the porter, and they had wrapped hand towels around them to keep them from soiling the counterpane.

"What's the idea?" said Johnny sitting up. "Oh, God!" He passed his hand over his eyes. His pulses were beating like triphammers against his temples. His head was roaring, his eye-lids burned and his mouth was as dry as a tanner's thumb.

"The idea," said Timberlake, "is that we've all got to scoot back to the airdrome."

"Why? We just got here."

"All leaves recalled, my boy. Your holiday's over. It's back to the trenches for you. You look like you had yourself a night. What happened to you?"

"I don't know. I passed out."

"The hell you did. How did you get back here?"

"Damned if I know."

"How do you feel?"

"Terrible."

"Send for the chilled tomatoes, boys. We've got a *blessé* on our hands."

John was struggling to remember the incidents of the last evening. Sylvia! That's how it began. The locket.

"Look at me," commanded Timberlake. "Don't you think I'm in pretty good repair?"

"Did you get your red pants?"

"Did I not! Let me tell you something, young man. Don't ever change pants with a man in Paris in war-time."

"Why?"

"Damned if I know. But you stick to your own pants. I got arrested and flung in the hoosegow. I traded pants with this fellow, see, and hats. I got a swell pair of red pants and a *képi* with a red top. We traded in an alley somewhere. As soon as I walked out on the street the M.P.'s nabbed me. Masquerading in a foreign uniform or something. Violation of some damn article of war or something. They chucked me in that damn military jail up by the Place Pigalle."

"How'd you get out?"

"Funny thing. They nabbed the fellow with my pants and hat about an hour later and threw him in the same tank. As soon as they had us together, they saw what had happened and they let us trade back. The Provost Marshal had orders to send me back to the field anyway; that's where I got my orders."

Could you imagine him carrying a girl's

picture all the way through the war, that belonged to somebody else? Johnny remembered how stunned he was to discover that it wasn't himself that Sylvia loved. Then he had felt ashamed, felt like crawling away and hiding his head for carrying that locket around with him so long. Dave had had the inside track all the time.

"Did you pass out cold?"

"Must have. I don't remember a damn thing."

And Johnny had felt sorry for Dave sometimes, because he, Johnny thought that he had the inside all the time. Could you beat that?

"Well, *somebody* must have brought you home."

Johnny, because his pride was hurt, felt that David had betrayed him. If Dave had really been his friend he would have told him, wouldn't he? Would have protected him. Would have put him wise.

It was when they were sitting down to the breakfast that David had ordered sent up to the room, that Timberlake discovered the silk stocking. It was lying on the floor beside the chair on which Mary's bundle had lain.

"Oh, ho!" he shouted, holding it up at full length.

They all regarded it with respectful interest.

"He passed out cold, did he? And he doesn't remember a damn thing. Doesn't even know how he got home? Too bad. I'll bet he can't even remember where this came from."

Despite the fact that among the war fliers there was no stigma attached to an amorous adventure in Paris, Johnny could conceal neither his surprise nor his embarrassment.

"*Souvenir!*" said Jimmie St. Ives, "That's what it is, a souvenir. He's collecting 'em, too."

"Maybe she left in a hurry."

"Maybe she's still here." They all started poking around in closets and looking under the bed.

"Can't imagine why she went off with

only one stocking on," said Timberlake. "Never heard of a girl doing that before."

"Well, are you going to explain this mystery, young man?"

"I don't know anything about it."

"Maybe it blew in over the transom."

They speculated airily about the presence of the silk stocking in Johnny's room.

"Aren't you going to open up?" said St. Ives. "Come on, Lieutenant, break down and tell us about it. Was she nice? Was it the blonde that tried to bite your ear off? She was certainly the make for you. Was she the one?"

Johnny was miserable. He felt that something irreparable had happened to him. They all thought he'd had a companion of the night. God, he wished he could remember what happened after the Folies Bergère.

He was miserable and embarrassed and ashamed and now he became sullen. He didn't care much what happened now. Now that he'd found out about Dave and Sylvia —and—after last night.

All the way back to the airdrome in the

car, he sat sullenly in the back seat and refused to speak to Dave. He sat with a hard, set face and unrelenting eyes. His friend, his flying mate. Nuts.

"I think old Joe Remorse is visiting him," Timberlake told St. Ives.

Though there had been no word and there would not be any, of course, until the very eve of the battle, since general orders had a curious way of penetrating the German intelligence, the pilots knew that a big offensive was brewing. That was the reason for the recall of all leaves. Every squadron in the sector was at full strength. Besides, the 39th had moved from Toul to a new airdrome up behind Verdun. This was in August, 1918.

One of the preliminary steps of the drive was to put out the eyes of the enemy. The German observation balloons which hung at two-mile intervals behind the German lines were fairly deep inside and they were ringed about with crack Archie batteries and expert high-angle gun crews.

Major Brand had two of them spotted and asked for balloon-strafers. Johnny Powell happened to be the first to see the order posted on the operations board and was the first to volunteer.

"I want two of you," the Major said, "who is your side-kick?"

"Armstrong." Johnny admitted unwillingly.

"Armstrong, oh yes, well ask him—" At that moment Armstrong himself appeared at the H.Q. office.

"Heard you wanted volunteers, sir," he said, "For balloon strafing."

The Major spread out a map on the table.

"Here they are," he pointed out, "D-6 and D-7. Powell, I want you to go in after them. Armstrong, you are to stay above and watch for enemy patrols. I don't want either of you to get in there and get cut off. Powell, you keep an eye on Armstrong; if he sees a squadron sneaking around behind he will fire a couple of red lights from his Verey pistol and you're to run for home. Understand?"

"Now take this map, both of you, and study it. You ought to be ready to start around six-thirty. Dusk is the best for this business."

Johnny took the map and Dave followed him over to the barracks. There he spread it out and the two bent over it. Johnny was busy tracing out his course when he heard Dave say:

"Listen, Johnny, would you do something for me?"

Johnny looked up without replying.

David unpinned the bronze decoration from his blouse. "Will you take this back to my mother? I want her to have it. Do you mind?"

"Take it back to your mother! Why not do it yourself?"

"I'm afraid I won't be able to."

"Why not, for God's sake?"

"I think — that — this — will — be — my —last—ride."

The grave, measured quality of his voice startled Johnny. There was final, absolute conviction in his words. He glanced quickly at his friend. David was not looking at Johnny. He was staring out of the window at the ships on the dead-line. His gray eyes were fixed, unseeing.

"Horse-radish," said Johnny roughly. He was chilled by the look of prescience in David's eyes.

"I've heard that people had—premonitions," said David, "but I never could believe it, quite. I thought it was just a sort of fear. I can understand now."

"You think you've got a premonition, huh?"

"I know I'm not coming back."

For a moment Johnny's heart went out to his old buddy. He wanted to cheer him up, console him, comfort him. Tell him it was all imagination. You couldn't tell what was going to happen. Nobody could tell what was going to happen. But the sharp memory of his humiliation came upon him and he choked off his feeling.

"He's yellow," said Johnny to himself. "Like he was in the wireless test. All this chittering about premonitions. That's a lot of horse-radish. He's got the wind-up is all."

Dave put down the medal gently on the map under Johnny's eyes.

"There is something else I wonder if you'd do for me too——"

"But you're not going to get killed!"

"Remember one night at San Diego. The time White crashed. We made a compact, remember? If I got mine first, you said you'd fix things up to send home. And I said I'd do the same for you."

"Uh-huh."

"Well, will you go through everything and see that—that it's all right for—my mother to have."

"But——"

"That's all she'll have, you see. And I wouldn't want her to find anything that might—you know—hurt her. Her memory of me."

"Letters and things?"

"Yes."

"Oh, sure."

David's features were pale. His forehead was moist and his lips were working.

"I've left my wings in the top tray of my trunk," he said, "I want Sylvia to have them. I wonder if you'll——

"Why—what's the matter?"

"Sylvia!" Johnny exclaimed. "You got a hell of a lot of nerve to talk to me about Sylvia.

"You know damn well what's the matter."

"No, I don't, Johnny."

"You two certainly made a sap out of me."

"Aw, Johnny, how can you say that?"

Johnny took the locket out of his pocket and tossed it across the table. "Here," he said, "this belongs to you."

David refused to see it. "Look at me, Johnny. Look at me."

The other would not meet his eyes. "You might have told me."

How could he have told him. How *could* he. In Johnny's pride, his wilfulness, he would have hated David, would have been uncomfortable with him, would never have forgiven him for taking Sylvia away from him. He knew he would lose his friendship, his confidence if he had told him. Far better to hazard it on the chance that Johnny would never find out what was in the back of the locket. All these things David wanted to tell Johnny. But Johnny's face was set and hard. He wouldn't look at Dave, he didn't want to listen.

"If—if you knew what our—our friendship meant to me, you wouldn't say things like that."

"A hell of a friend you turned out to be."

"Ah, Johnny——"

"And as far as I'm concerned you can go to hell!"

A swift shadow pain fell across Armstrong's pale, sensitive features. "You don't mean that," he said painfully. "You don't mean that. Why, Johnny——"

"All set, boys?" Major Brand was coming through the doorway. "Get into your togs."

"You don't mean that."

Johnny turned his back, walked over to his cot and took down his combination suit from the hook on the wall. He dressed sullenly, without looking up, without exchanging a word.

"Your compass course is damn near due east," said the major, "you can guide on the stacks of the brick factory going out."

"Suppose the sausages are down," said Johnny, "shall we shoot up the place?"

"You've got six hundred rounds of tracers and incendiaries. Use your own judgment. But one thing," he added emphatically, "keep your eye on Armstrong and watch for his Verey lights. I don't want to lose a couple of pilots just now."

"Right you are, skipper." The hell with Armstrong and his Verey lights.

Dave followed Johnny out to the deadline. Their ships stood side by side, the motors turning. It was just getting dusk.

Dave climbed into the cockpit, tightened the chin-strap of his helmet, slipped down his goggles. His motor was turning over sweetly.

"All set?"

Johnny was buckling his safety belt.

"All set?"

Johnny rev'ed up his motor. The mechanics pulled out the wheel-chocks.

"All set!" Dave raised his arm.

Without so much as turning his head, or glancing over at his team-mate, Johnny gave his ship the gun and shot down the field into the wind.

The arm upraised over Dave's head fell to his lap. For a moment his head drooped, as from a blow. Then his body stiffened, he opened up his motor and followed the *Shooting Star* down the field. It seemed as if his ship never would get off the ground. Johnny had gone off without giving him the all set signal.

An orderly, sweeping the floor about Armstrong's cot, bent down and picked up a little furry rabbit with shoe-button eyes and a broken ear. Holy Christopher! Lieutenant Armstrong had gone off without his mascot. He ran for the doorway. Even before he crossed the room he saw whisht—whisht— two planes flash across the panel of light. Armstrong was in the air and his talisman was on the ground. The orderly tossed the rabbit over on the tautly drawn blanket of David's cot.

So David flew off that late August afternoon under a trilogy of dark omens. He flew off with a prescience of disaster, he flew off estranged from his team-mate, he flew off without his talisman.

There it lay on his cot, staring up at the ceiling with its idiotic, shoe-button eyes.

PART V

THE BLACK CROSS

PART V

THE BLACK CROSS

IT was the first time that the two had flown
off together without exchanging a preliminary wave of the hand. Johnny had
climbed into the *Shooting Star* and started
down the field without so much as turning
his head or holding up his hand for the all
set signal.

He looked neither to the right nor to the
left, his manner said: If you're going to follow me old man you'll have to hurry because
I'm on my way.

Many of the pilots had come out into the
field and gathered about in knots discussing
Powell's chances and watching the horizon.

At about seven-ten they should see a red
glow to the Southeast—and if all went well
they might see another a couple of miles further along.

Johnny flew as if he were alone; he sailed low over the poplars, clipping the tops of the trees and steeple-chasing across the fields. The *Shooting Star* was the faster ship, largely because Johnny spent much of his time in the hangar working on his motor.

Since he had come back from Paris they had all noticed the difference in him. The fresh grin was gone from his face and the guileless look from his eye.

"What the hell is bothering Powell these days?"

"Damned if I know. He's certainly on the warpath."

"Damned if not. Well, it won't be long now, the way he's flying."

Since Paris, Johnny had flown as one possessed of the demon of the Gadarine swine. When he wasn't in the air he was in the hangars working on his motor, overhauling his guns, trueing up his wings with a spirit level. He would not trust his plane to the mechanics, nor his guns to the armorers. His own hands were far more skillful than theirs. He wanted every mechanical part

A Paramount Picture.

DOUGHBOYS AND TANKS EVER ADVANCING, SUPPORTED BY THE WHIR OF WINGING AIRPLANES.

Wings.

A Paramount Picture. *Wings.*

POWELL LEAPS THROUGH THE OPENING TORN IN THE HOUSE BY THE ENEMY
PLANE HE SHOT DOWN.

to function faultlessly in this business of killing Huns.

He was a killer alright. It had begun to show in his face. There was a savageness in his eyes and certain relentlessness about his lips. His manner was nervous and quick. He was easily irritated and was capable of swift, black rages as Herman Schwimpf found out the day he failed to strain the gas through a chamois-skin and Johnny came home with a sputtering motor.

While he was on the ground he smoked cigarettes incessantly. He was in for a case of nerves as the flight surgeon could see.

"Powell didn't drink when he first came up here, did he?"

"No. Nor smoke either."

"Well, he's sure hitting it up now."

Powell was burning himself up, they all agreed. He was having almost daily combats, and in a single week he had brought down two Pfalz scouts, an Albatross and an L.V.G. He never saw a sausage balloon that he didn't go down and try to touch it off.

Now, as he flew along he did not throttle

down for his escort but continued at top flying speed. He didn't begin to climb until he was well away from the airdrome and then he only went to six hundred meters, just high enough to give him a dive on the drachen.

The hell with Armstrong, he'd have to look out for himself. No time for weak sisters.

At seven-ten to the dot the watchers at the airdrome saw a bright spot on the skyline, saw it blossom into a red glow which lighted up the whole sky to the Southeast.

Powell had got his first balloon!

Four minutes later a twin glow appeared to the left.

They slapped each other on the back. Could you beat that bird? Destroyed two balloons in four minutes. A balloon was worth two planes any day. The boy was certainly good. He must have stirred up a hornets' nest though. Have to get the hell out of there right now.

Minutes later a single plane appeared out

of the dusk, circled once over the field and landed.

When the mechanics ran up a voice called out.

"Armstrong back?"

"Not yet, sir."

The pilots rushed over to congratulate him, handed him out of his ship, chaired him on their shoulders and carried him over to the quarters. But for the first time since they had known him, they saw an expression of anxiety on his face.

The same question kept returning to his lips. Dave back?

Oh, he probably got lost in the dark on the way home; landed in a field somewhere. He'd call up before long and tell them where he was.

A half-hour and, hour went by and darkness settled over the airdrome, Armstrong had not come back. They lighted gasoline flares on the landing field and waited.

Johnny went out on the field, talked with the mechanics, his eyes staring into the encircling darkness.

Major Brand couldn't get much of the story from him. He had followed his map-prepared course straight as an arrow and come directly onto the first balloon. They were just reeling it down for the night. The Archie battery had set up a hell of clatter but Johnny had put a stream of incendiary bullets into the bag before they got his range.

His dive had carried him past the balloon right down to within fifty feet of the ground. He had turned and streaked it along the ground for D 7.

Had he seen any Verey lights from Armstrong?

No, he had gone straight for the second balloon. He had zoomed up under it and speared it even before the observer jumped.

No, he didn't see Armstrong at all. The sky was empty when he turned back and he thought Armstrong had gone home.

Herman Schwimpf kept the flares lighted throughout the night and patrolled back and forth in front of the hangars, firing Verey pistol lights.

At intervals throughout the night

Johnny, with a top-coat thrown over his pajamas, appeared on the field to strain his eyes into the darkness to listen for the sound of a motor.

Herman couldn't believe that anything could have affected Johnny so, the reckless, irresponsible Johnny Powell, the wild man of the 39th.

Neither he nor anyone else knew what Johnny had on his conscience. Johnny alone knew that he hadn't watched for Verey pistol flares from Armstrong's ship, as he had been instructed. He had simply left Armstrong to fare for himself, and if anything had happened to him——

Armstrong did not come back that night or any other night. The sky had swallowed him up as completely as it had Guynemer on the afternoon in September, 1917, when he flew off toward Poelcappelle and never came back.

For three days Johnny did not leave the fliers' quarters. They tried to comfort him, one by one, Timberlake, St. Ives, Jimmie Holabird.

"Don't brood over it, old man. He's probably a prisoner. You'll hear from him sooner or later."

But Johnny would not be consoled. He sat on the edge of his cot, with his head in his hands and gazed in upon his own heart. He didn't know how firmly he was attached to Dave until Dave was gone. He remembered the look in Dave's eyes that day, and he felt that Dave would never come back.

What was the use of anything? What was there left now? Dave was gone.

Sylvia meant nothing any more. There was nothing for him back home. Anyway that night in Paris had made a difference.

Well, one thing he could do, and that was shoot down a lot of Germans. That was about all he was good for now, anyway. He didn't care, by God, if he lived or died.

When he came out of the mental stupor that followed the shock of the loss of his flying mate, he threw himself into the fighting with insane energy.

It was Major Brand who stumbled on the

truth or what he suspected to be the truth about Armstrong's disappearance. He had been on a trip up to the front lines and stopped at Mivelle on the way back.

The village of Mivelle had been in German hands up until the last offensive. The townspeople were extremely voluble and fairly dripped stories of the incidents of the German occupation.

Major Brand was having supper by himself in a tiny estaminet in the village, when one of the villagers, an elderly Frenchman, noting the silver wings on his blouse, volunteered an account of the sad end, or what he took to be the end, of an American flier.

It had happened just at dusk, *croyez-vous*. There had been a fight off to the west. Two balloons afire. Followed a running fight between five Fokkers and one with the French cocarde. He was clever that one. He sent one Boche spinning out of the sky and down in flames.

That was that orange streak he had seen across the sky, thought Major Brand.

The other four had left off the fight and

turned home. But something was wrong with the Spad pilot. He flew strangely, as if he were lost or wounded.

It was a wound, the villager thought, because the pilot made for the grain field by the river outside the town. You know how one thirsts when one is wounded? One makes for water. Well, the field by the river was in German territory. The pilot did not know that, evidently. He landed, not a bad landing. Got out of his plane and started for the river.

The Boches came out of the woods around and called upon him to surrender. He went back to his plane, and lit a fuse to it.

Surrender! No, the American whipped out his pistol and began firing at them. Brave he was, that one. Like a lion. They shot him down, of course.

Some Frenchwomen came out of the village with sheets to wind around the body. The German Captain, what a brute, would not let them go near. He ordered a wooden cart from the village. The women came with armfuls of straw to put in it. He ordered them away.

No, they did not see him buried. No, he could not remember the number of the plane. It was all burned up. An American he was, by the uniform.

"Well, if he were dead, wouldn't they have buried him nearby?"

"Possibly."

"He may be still alive then."

The Frenchman shrugged his shoulders.

There was little doubt in the Major's mind that this was Armstrong. But it was no good speculating about his fate since there was no way of knowing how serious were his wounds.

He decided not to tell Powell. Powell was going great guns at the moment and there was no knowing what the news might do to him. It could only unsettle him, since the story was inconclusive, and only aggravate the mystery of his real end. As far as Powell was concerned no news was good news. Let it remain like that. The International

Red Cross would report Armstrong sooner
or later if he was a casualty.

The boy who occupied the cot next to
Armstrong's at the German field hospital
behind Thiancourt was a member of the Yale
unit and had been flying at Dunkirk. He
had been shot down and his jaw was broken
in three places. His name was Starling; he
had escaped from a German prison camp
once before and he was fiercely determined
to do it again.

He had a tiny dial compass and a German
railway map sewn in the lining of his blouse.
He had a dozen schemes but he favored the
most immediate one.

"We'll be evacuated to a prison camp in a
couple of days," he said one morning after
the nurse had finished dressing his face,
"pretty deep in Germany. As soon as I find
out which one it is,—goddam this jaw—I'll
look up the route on the map, see what line
we take. We ought to be able to jump off
that train somewhere along the line. At
night maybe, or in a tunnel. Tunnels are

the things, my boy." Starling had made his first escape via a railway tunnel, and had great faith in them.

They did not wait for Starling's jaw to knit, or David's wounds to heal. He had two; one from an explosive bullet in the fleshy part of his thigh, the one that brought him down by the river; the other was a rifle-bullet wound in the shoulder. The field hospital was for emergency cases; at the first signs of healing, the men were shifted back into Germany. As Starling had prophesied they were evacuated about the same time.

But try as he would, Starling could not learn to what camp they were being sent. They were put on the train under two guards, neither of whom spoke English.

Starling tested them carefully by firing insults at them and observing their facial expressions. There was no faintest glimmer of understanding.

"These sod-busters are safe," Starling said. "Now if we're going to make a break we've got to do it quick. God knows where we're going or how long it'll take us to get there. Before we know it we'll be inside a prison camp and then we'll have a hell of a time getting out.''

Starling carefully observed the names of the villages they passed, and after awhile got permission to go into the car lavatory.

While one of the guards sat outside with his rifle between his knees, Starling got out his map and studied it.

''I know what line we're on,'' he told Armstrong when he came back to his seat. ''We go through a tunnel just the other side of Luxbourg.''

Starling proceeded to outline the plot in detail. Just after the train passed through the town Armstrong was to go to the lavatory. He could lock the door on the inside and escape through the window when they hit the tunnel. The window was small, but Armstrong, who was smaller than Starling, could get through it. The train wouldn't be rolling fast because they would be leaving the village.

Starling would complain of lack of air

and go out on the observation platform.
Once in the darkness of the tunnel he would
sock the guard in the jaw and jump off the
rear of the train. They could hide in the
tunnel till nightfall and then slip off into
the woods.

"I'll give you the high-sign when it's time
to get up," said Starling.

Because it was going away from the lines
and carrying nothing but prisoners, the train
made way for everything rolling up to the
front and consequently made slow progress,
which was, as Starling pointed out, a great
help.

They stood for two hours on a side line
outside Luxbourg, and entered the mouth of
the tunnel at half-speed. Starling nodded
his head and they both arose.

Inside the lavatory, Armstrong bolted the
door, and pried open the window with the
buckle of his Sam Brown belt.

He forced himself, head first, through the
aperture, breathed a short prayer, and dived.
Cinders tore his skin and flew into his mouth
as he rolled over and over the road-bed.

The train rumbled by and he found himself alone in the smoke-filled darkness.

"Starling! Starling! Starling!"

The tunnel was dark and empty as a tomb. What could have happened to Starling? The train did not stop. Dave was doomed to go on alone. The worst of it was the plunge to the road-bed had opened up his wounds.

He hid inside the West end of the tunnel until nightfall, when he slipped out and made his first meal off raw cabbages in a field on the outskirts of the town.

Without a map or a compass he knew it was hopeless to strike for the Swiss frontier. He could never make it across Germany.

And without map or compass or any means of obtaining information or direction without risking immediate arrest, Starling's ingenious escape developed into a series of disjointed wanderings for Armstrong.

He hid in thickets and slept during the day, and travelled and foraged by night. Dogs were the worst, children and dogs. A dozen times they barked out his presence and sent him scampering back into the darkness. Children on their eternal stick-gathering excursions into the woods came within a few feet of his hiding places.

He might have had to give himself up in the end on account of his wounds, which had gone bad, if he hadn't stumbled onto the German airdrome back of Treves.

The flying field was skirted by a thick growth of young firs which afforded excellent cover. The idea of attempting to escape in a German plane came to Armstrong from the first moment he discovered his proximity to the field.

It was a desperate measure, a mad, extreme, outside chance, but it presented the only possible means of escape to one whose case was already hopeless.

For three days Dave lay in the trees a few feet from the high wire fence that encircled the field. For three days he watched the ships rolled out from the hangars, tuned up and sent off on patrol. It was a Jagdstaffel unit, a famous German fighting group, flying black-and-white checkered Fokkers.

Thank God, it was an attack squadron, flying single-seaters. Dave felt sure he could take one of them off the ground no matter how unfamiliar the controls might be. Stealing a bomber would have been a different dish of tea for a chasse-trained pilot.

Dave could hear the guttural speech of the mechanics, the laughter of the pilots; from his listening post he became acquainted with the routine, the personnel, the equipment of the field. He gradually worked himself around to a position opposite the end of the dead line, within short striking distance of the point where the last ship of the formation usually stood! There must come a minute, sometime, when the end plane would be left unattended, with its motor running.

At night with a sharp stick he dug a shallow hole under the fence, through which he would slip when the moment came.

In all his thinking and planning there was one thing that you would think would have occurred to him first; that the black-crossed ship which he flew might be attacked by his own men, the moment he flew within his own lines.

A Paramount Picture. *Wings.*

TRIUMPH TURNS TO GRIEF AS POWELL REALIZES HE HAS SHOT DOWN HIS
DEAREST FRIEND.

A Paramount Picture. *Wings.*

AS POWELL BERATES HIMSELF, ARMSTRONG FORGIVES HIS PAL FOR THE MISTAKE
THAT IS RESULTING FATALLY.

The St. Mihiel Drive, as any of the boys
from the 2nd Division will tell you, was the
initial operation of the First American
Army.

The St. Mihiel salient penetrated the
French lines, like a macaw's beak, to a
depth of fifteen miles. Bavarian troops had
captured the city of St. Mihiel, lying twenty
miles east of Verdun, in the first days of the
war and in four years no counter-attack had
been able to dislodge them.

The Hun defenses were well-nigh impene-
trable. During their years of occupation
they had been unceasingly busy at strength-
ening their trench-works, wire and fortifica-
tions.

Out of the left side of the wedge rose one
of the most celebrated hills along the Front:
Montsec. Montsec, cone-topped and lofty,
bristling with artillery, shot through with
fox-holes, swarming with soldiery, Montsec
with its concrete dug-outs, its tunnels, its
observation posts looked down upon the
plains beneath and dominated the area.

A half-dozen lines of closely-drawn defenses, one inside the other, girdled the foot of the hill. Not an airplane had left the Toul airdrome in two years that hadn't been followed by German eyes through binoculars atop the crest. When General Pershing first sighted Montsec he said, "We must have that eminence."

But the slopes of Montsec were bathed in the blood of French infantrymen who had gone against it in desperate, futile assaults.

Three times had the French stormed the heights; three times had they been swept down by hot hurricanes of machine-gun fire, and the contour of the salient had changed but a few hundred meters.

Montsec had an evil reputation. When the doughboys in the First Division learned that they were to walk around the foot of Montsec they cocked their tin hats over their left eyes and whistled thoughtfully. Thirty thousand Frogs had been killed there in the fall of 1916 for the privilege of holding the ground for twenty minutes.

There were a number of good reasons for reducing the salient. It was the first necessary step in an American offensive. It would forever remove the menace to Verdun. It would release 150 miles of French territory and a city of 100,000 people. It would open up the way to Metz, the Briey Iron Basin and the Metz-Sedan Railroad.

Though the plans for the operation were guarded with the usual military secrecy, there were few who did not know of the intention of the Americans to attack. It was openly discussed in Paris; the Swiss journals guessed at the date—and missed it by twenty-four hours—and General von Gallwitz, watching from the top of Montsec, observed the abnormal activity going on behind the American lines and anticipated what was coming.

The staff officers of the First American Army worked out the details of the Drive, calling upon every useful factor in the entire American machinery of war. They placed and scheduled the engineers, the gas and flame regiments, the ammunition and supply trains, cavalry, water supply, motor transport and prisoner cages. Few battles have been planned with such minute care or brought off with such clock-work precision as the St. Mihiel Drive. There were 75,000 Huns in that salient, heavily fortified, generously armed and supplied with artillery, machine guns and vast stores of ammunition. A stiff resistance was expected.

The roads leading to the American front were loaded night after night with troops on the march; all of the American battle elements were in flow toward the lines. The secret concentration of scattered divisions, supplies and munitions had begun as early as August 20.

The word went out that "D" day was to be Sept. 12 and that 5 A.M. was to be "H" hour. Just at dusk, therefore, on the 11th, everything began to move at once. And just at dusk the rain began a cold, steady downpour that continued all through the night.

The men of the 82nd, 90th, 5th and 2nd Divisions were deployed along the southern face of the salient. To their left were the 42nd, 89th and 1st. To these two Army Corps was entrusted the task of delivering the principal smash. Masses of reserves were moved into the area throughout the night and were screened in the woods when daylight came.

It was a long column of French Renault baby tanks, piloted by Americans, that led the general movement into the front lines that night. Batteries of artillery moved out from under cover and took positions in the mud-filled and abandoned trenches far out in front. Then came the infantry, to lie all night in the slimy mud of the marshes below Montsec awaiting "H" hour. *"Jee*sis but wasn't it cold. . . ."

At one o'clock on the morning of the 12th, the American artillery spaced along the front as far as the eye could reach, cut loose with the first crashing notes of the four-day chorus of war. A sheet of flame, along an endless line, burst the pitch black darkness of the night. " 'member when they opened up. . . ."

For four solid hours the gun crews hurled fourteen-inch shells across the marshes, pounding the German wire to bits and bursting in the trench-works. "Say, boy, we certainly threw over a lot of stuff *that* night. . . ."

Just at five, when a gray murky light began to seep into the lowlands the gun batteries left off the violent long-range preparation and switched to a creeping barrage. Up went the stout-hearted engineers to blow hell out of the wire entanglements with their Bangalore Torpedoes.

Following closely behind the advancing crescent of shell-bursts and supported by the tanks, came the infantry, men of the First and Fourth Corps who had lain all night in the swamps and who looked like drowned rats as they plodded along, soaking wet and plastered from head to foot with slimy yellow clay.

They plugged steadily along and wondered when the hell the Germans were going to open up on them from the heights. They continued straight on and fell upon the Huns in the first trenches in the middle of the fog.

That murderous fire from the hill-top never came. The fact of the matter was that the Germans were pulling out of the salient as fast as they could. Von Gallwitz had been unable to obtain the release of reserves from any other portion of the Western front and he knew that he could not stand against the 40,000 Americans advancing against Mont-sec.

True there were several stubborn German gun crews who stuck to their positions and continued firing into the advancing waves of infantry but they were soon flanked and silenced.

Regulars and marines of the 2nd Division who had been at Belleau Wood in July and who had heard the deadly crackle of ten belt-fed, water-cooled Maxim machine guns at once and knew what real German resistance was, said that St. Mihiel was a walk-over. The Americans captured 16,000 prisoners, 448 guns of all calibres and vast stores of munitions and supplies and they took Montsec like Grant took Richmond.

But it was no walk-over to the men of the 82nd, lads from Pennsylvania and Vermont and New Hampshire who advanced astride the Moselle. The Huns were not retreating on this flank. Machine-gunners, nested in the hills east of the river, opened up with a withering enfilade fire and mowed them down. Twelve hundred of them fell there and did not get up again.

It was no walk-over for the men of the 42nd Rainbow Division who cut their way through the ugly snarl of caves, trenches, barbed wire and machine gun nests that made up the Bois de Sonnard. When the brigade reformed on the other side of the wood there were six hundred empty files.

It was no push-over to the six thousand lads from Texas and Oklahoma and Missouri and Kansas and Nebraska who went down in the mud of Northeastern France during those four days.

The St. Mihiel Drive saw the greatest massing of aircraft ever attained on the Western front. Apart from the two squadrons with the British, every American pursuit plane was ordered into action. Day reconnaissance was entrusted to the 91st

Aero Squadron. Four French squadrons regulated the fire of the American long range guns. All five American Pursuit Groups were sent into the air.

It so happened that there was but one good day for flying in the four days that it took to smash the salient. And yet American observation planes penetrated the fog and low-hanging clouds and gales of wind and rain to a distance of sixty kilometers behind Montsec.

Bombing pilots brought their big planes so close to the ground that the Huns might have knocked them down with a tomato can. The pursuit pilots ranged the clouds over the entire arena of battle. Allied aircraft swept the skies.

In his cot in the flier's quarters in the airdrome behind Verdun Johnny Powell was wakened by the dull concussions of the big guns at one in the morning of the 12th.

At five he was fully dressed and out in the mess hall pleading with Major Brand to let him take off. It was noon before the Major let him go and even then the clouds were scarcely six hundred feet high and the visibility was soup-thick.

Johnny flew out, crossed the Meuse and turned toward Verdun. Beneath him rose the smoke pillars of the retreating Huns.

Ammunition dumps, food stores, supplies, villages, haystacks were all burning in his wake. Johnny knew that it was not the intention of the Americans to take Montsec by frontal attack. They were sweeping around it to an objective point behind and so isolate it. The objective was the village of Vigneulles.

Johnny turned the nose of the *Shooting Star* toward Vigneulles and saw that highway running back to the fortified city of Metz was choked with German guns, cars, trucks and soldiers all in full retreat. Here was fair game. Swooping down over the column he opened up with both his guns. In a moment the orderly mass was in a mad scrambling uproar. Horses and men broke and ran for the trees and ditches. For a quarter of a mile the road was a shambles.

One of his incendiary bullets set a covered truck on fire and it went careening down the road blazing furiously.

Of all the pursuit planes that swarmed over the field of battle during the four days of the St. Mihiel Drive, none was more swift or flashing than a silver Spad with a shooting star painted on its fuselage.

During those four days Powell was seen at the airdrome only at short intervals; when he came back for ammunition, to refill his tank, to repair a rocker arm, to clear a gun jam.

He was aflame with the fever of battle. He was killing, killing, and he was in his element. He strafed the German third line trenches at the foot of the hill, and he shot up the Hun artillery positions masked behind Montsec.

He raked a platoon of Hun engineers off a pontoon bridge thrown across the Mad River above Thiaucourt.

A cluster of Hun lineman repairing a break on a telegraph pole, tumbled to the ground like fat bees when Powell dived down on them east of St. Benoit.

He was all over the sky and everywhere about the ground, flying, shooting with hellish glee. He would get killed, he must get killed before it was over. And this was the way he wanted to die, by God, in the very thick of it.

Just off the corner of the Apremont Forest he espied a lone German plane winging its way along the ground straight for the American lines. The white puffs from American anti-aircraft fire were showing all about it. It was a Fokker and it bore the checker-board markings of a Jagdstaffel group.

That fellow had nerve—to come over so low! He was flying in a straight line too. Well this would be Johnny's eighteenth victory.

Johnny came down on him like a rocket, —and missed with his first burst. You would expect a hot combat with a pilot who would fly right into the enemy lines. Instead, this one banked out of the line of fire and continued straight on.

Johnny regained his height and dove again. And again he missed, and again the Hun pilot refused battle. It resolved itself into a chase, the one plane pursuing, while the other dodged about and headed deeper into the lines.

It could not last long, Johnny was too good a pilot, and too expert a shot to miss a man he had practically driven into the ground.

Just before he fired the fatal rounds, he thought he saw the Hun pilot waving his hand as if trying to signal something. It was just another Hun trick, of course, Johnny got him in his ring sights and tripped his triggers.

The Fokker tilted uncertainly, fell off on a wing and crashed to the earth in the orchard of a farm-house near Mivelle tearing away a section of the white picket fence in its fall.

Swooping low over the fallen plane,

Johnny could see his fallen foe lying in the wreckage. And he noticed for the first time that he wore neither helmet nor goggles.

At ten o'clock on the evening of September 14, 1918 Major Brand was seated at his desk in headquarters going over the pilots' reports. The telephone rang. It was Captain Black of the American Red Cross.

"Say, Major, a Lieutenant named Armstrong belong to your outfit?"

"Yes. Been missing."

"We picked him up today."

"Where?"

"Mivelle. In a German plane."

"A *German* plane!"

"Yes. Evidently trying to fly it back inside the lines."

"Dead?"

"Yes, Major. Shot down. Body's in the church over here now. Coming over?"

"Right away. Sure it's Armstrong?"

"David Armstrong, 39th Aero Squadron, First Pursuit Group, that's how his tag reads."

The Major hung up. Of all pitiful, terrible things. Dave Armstrong shot down by his own men.

On the report sheet in front of him his eyes caught the paragraph——

"——*shot down Fokker out of control in orchard one-half mile east of Mivelle,* 4:30 P.M.

> *Signed, John Powell,*
> *2nd Lt. A.S. U.S.A.*"

God in Heaven! Powell had claimed the death ship.

PART VI

THE RECKONING

fused to go. The major went back alone to the airdrome.

Achilles did not watch beside the dead Patrocles more steadfastly than did John Powell beside his friend. Throughout the long September night he kept tearless vigil over the body of his comrade.

". . . so it had broken asunder the richest bough on the tree of his life; the most generous part of himself ruined. For him the beauty of war had diminished, now that he was no longer to see, burning in those dead eyes, the fervor of effort, the security of resolution. He was no longer to taste the two purest joys of a manly heart: steadiness of eye in attack and the pride of watching over a beloved peer."

The Chaplain of the 39th found him there when he came in the morning.

They gave David a flier's funeral. His burial, like his death, was of brief and tragic beauty. The little church was filled with flowers, wreaths of heavy, fragrant French roses. There was one, from the

mechanics of the 39th, fashioned in the shape
of a broken propeller blade.

A battalion of regulars from the 2nd Division came over as an escort. They stood
at present arms when six of the dead flier's
friends carried the body from the chapel to
the gun carriage in the narrow street in
front of the church.

The procession formed behind the Division band which struck up the sombre
strains of the Dead March and led the way to
the little green cemetery beyond the village.
The escort marched behind the music, followed by the chaplain. John Powell walked
among those who followed the caisson.

The column filed through the gates of the
cemetery and halted beside the new grave.
The flag-draped coffin was carried in front
of the escort and placed over the grave while
the soldiers stood at present arms and the
others stood with uncovered heads.

Chaplain Cairns stepped forward and in a
resolute voice committed the body of David
Armstrong to its last resting place. Overhead the airplanes wheeled and circled.

They had flown over, the pilots of the 39th Pursuit, with muffled motors to pay their final respect to their dead brother.

A moment before the body was lowered out of sight the dark shadow of an airplane passed silently over the rose-strewn bier. It was like a caress.

The dead flier's ears did not hear the voice of the Lieutenant ordering the farewell salute from the rifles. The muzzles of the pieces were elevated as three vollies rang out over the grave. Nor could he hear the clear calm notes of the bugle sounding taps.

Gliding low over the heads of the mourners came the pilots in their nervous, dancing little Spads to drop flowers on the grave. The procession wound out of the cemetery. John Powell was the last to leave, alone, a solitary figure, rigid and dry-eyed.

John Powell carried out his pact with his dead friend. He collected, with stumbling, uncertain fingers, Armstrong's things to be sent home. They weren't things any more, they were *effects*. God, oh, God!

Under the top tray of Dave's trunk he

found the bundles of letters from Sylvia. He read only one, the last.

"—*Why can't he understand? And why can't you tell him, dear heart? I feel so dreadfully guilty letting him go on thinking as he does. It is so hard for me to know what to do. His letters are so confident and unknowing. I can hardly bear reading them, and they are so difficult to answer.*

"*You say that he is your dearest friend now and nothing could bring you to hurt him. But you—we—must hurt some time. Surely he must be told before he comes back.*

"*If only he could understand. He is so willful and so thoughtless and so blind. Why can't he see that Mary Preston is the only person in the whole world for him. She adores him, has adored him for years. No one else ever will love him as she does. If he loses her love he will lose the most precious thing that he could ever possess.*

"*Has he changed any? Is he as wild as ever? Of course he is quite famous now, with the newspapers and all, and everyone here is so proud of him. Of you both.*

"*When, oh when will this dreadful war be over? If you could only know what it means*

*to us, to your father and your dear mother,
and me, to have you in constant danger at
the front.*

*"We live in awful suspense, from day to
day, from hour to hour. I am with your
mother, dear one, much of the time now, and
if you see the frightened look in her eyes
every time the telephone rings or the mail
arrives you would stop flying the minute the
war is over and come to her—and to me.*

*"She is so brave and your father is so
composed but I know that they can't hold
up much longer.*

*"I pray for you every night, blessed one;
God watch over you and keep you safe and
send you back to us. . . ."*

Johnny could read no further. The Major
saw the candle burning in the little two-cot
cubicle at midnight and found Johnny sitting on the floor with his head down on Armstrong's locker trunk. He put him to bed
and blew out the light. The Major had never
seen anyone grieve so for a dead comrade.

Timberlake was talking to St. Ives in the
shadow of a hangar.

"Say have you noticed Powell lately?"

"You mean since the—since the accident? Poor kid he certainly took a terrible wallop."

"No, I mean about his hair."

"His hair? No."

"It's growing in gray."

"The *hell* it is!"

"You know I've heard that people's hair sometimes turns white after a great scare or sickness or accident or something and I thought that was a lot of hooey. But I swear this kid's hair is turning. Take a look the next time you see him."

"You know I don't think they ought to let him fly much more. He's lost his zip. He'll get knocked off."

"I don't think he cares much if he does."

"They ought to take him off flying."

"The skipper told me he wouldn't let him go out alone any more."

"That's a good idea."

"And that he was going to make him a patrol leader. You know, take the youngsters out on their first trip over the lines."

"He'd be damn fine for that."

"Sure he would. I bet he wouldn't lose a pilot. But take a look at his hair the next time you see him. Around his temples."

For Johny Powell the beauty of war had diminished.

Temple, Wash., welcomed back its most celebrated citizen on an afternoon in early January, 1919.

They gave him such a reception as befitted a son who had gone forth and brought distinction to the town. The Temple flier, the famous balloon-strafer of the 39th Aero Squadron, First Pursuit Group, U. S. Army, was back to his own. Eighteen air victories to his credit. The Croix de Guerre with three palms. Few communities could boast such a hero.

Lieutenant Powell stepped off the train into a swirl of excited townspeople. His mother was the first to reach him and she held him until his father interposed. Then his father kissed him. A year ago Johnny would have been ashamed, ashamed at his father's emotion and at his mother's tears.

The Mayor's committee of welcome escorted him through the station and, to his great embarrassment, handed him into the cock-pit of a dummy airplane blanketed in flowers and towed behind a truck. They pulled him through the streets of Temple to the new auditorium.

In the eyes of the townspeople Dean Powell's son had found himself and come home a hero. But John Powell was no hero to himself. He felt that he had lost himself.

Throughout the speeches at the auditorium he sat looking distantly over the heads of the gathering, with his hand in the pocket of his blouse, fingering Armstrong's decoration. Nor did he, to the wonderment of many, take off his overseas cap.

He did not see the Armstrongs anywhere. Of course, they wouldn't be there. They couldn't have borne it. This joyous reception to a returning aviator.

The faces of his mother and father, alight with pride, smiled up at him from the first row of seats.

Mary-Louise was in the auditorium. She

stood in one of the crowded side aisles, far back from the platform. He had caught a glimpse of her.

When finally the speeches and the hand-shaking were over and the gathering broke up into scattered knots, Mary saw Johnny walk over to where Sylvia stood, alone, saw him take her quietly by the arm and draw her away.

Mary-Louise turned and left the building.

Johnny had two things to do. One was to see Sylvia and the other was to go to the Armstrong's.

"I know all about everything," he told Sylvia directly. "I know about the locket and you and Dave. I'm sorry I didn't know before, before——

"He was a fine fellow—Dave. Finest there ever was, or will be.

"He was thinking about you, when he went off the last time. He wanted you to have these."

Johnny placed Dave's wings and silver identification disk in Sylvia's hand.

Sylvia could scarcely speak. "You're—going—to see his mother—aren't you?"

Johnny tightened his lips. "I'm going there now."

Erect and soldierly, he walked up the long white steps of the Armstrong house.

Dave's mother was seated in a chair beside one of the tall French windows in the living room. One of the panels of the window was darkened by a red silk square with a gold star in its center.

Dave's father sat in a wheel chair on the far side of the room. They said he had suffered a stroke.

John Powell walked toward the mother and halted uncertainly in the center of the floor.

Mrs. Armstrong arose, walked toward him. She wondered why he stood so, why he didn't speak, why he didn't take off his overseas cap. Was he the same thoughtless youth who had gone away two years before?

As she approached him, she saw his hand go up timidly, self-consciously.

He was looking anxiously into her face.

When he uncovered himself Mrs. Armstrong saw that his hair had grown in a gray, steel gray.

"Oh, my boy——"

His hair which had been so intensely black, was now prematurely turned. There was no need for him to try to explain to her what he had gone through.

The tragic experience which he had undergone was stamped permanently upon his being. The halo-like aspect of his hair gave his dark eyes a luminous, poignant quality.

Mrs. Armstrong drew him over to a chair by the window.

In slow, timid hesitant words he tried to tell her the story. And as he talked it was the mother who comforted the boy—not the boy who comforted the mother.

"He knew that he was going out for the last time," John said. "He told me before we started off together. I wouldn't believe him. He told me to take his Croix de Guerre back to you." Johnny drew the medal from his pocket and gave it to her.

"Well . . . he didn't come back. And it

was my fault. I am to blame. I was to watch
for his signals. And I didn't, I went in
after another balloon.

"They attacked him and I wasn't there to
help. They brought him down. He landed
near Mivelle. When they told him to surrender he shot it out with them—with the
German soldiers. The people in Mivelle told
us about it afterwards."

He was talking calmly enough but Mrs.
Armstrong knew that his voice was choking
up.

"They shot him and he was sent to a German hospital and then to a prison camp. On
the way he escaped—a boy named Starling
from Yale wrote the whole thing to Major
Brand. Starling was stabbed with a bayo-
net when he tried to get away.

"Nobody knows what happened to Dave
after that until he stole a German plane and
flew back into our lines.

"I don't know if you know the truth or
not. Major Brand said he would write and
tell you. Dave was shot down by one of us.

"Mrs. Armstrong — Mrs. Armstrong,

please don't hate me—it was I who did it—
I was the one. . . ."

Johnny was on his knees beside her, his
head in his hands, his shoulders moving un-
controllably.

Mrs. Armstrong was stroking his head
with gentle hands.

"There, there, it doesn't matter now
how it happened. It doesn't matter. You
must be brave, my boy, as we are trying to be
brave. You must forget—life must go on—
you must go on."

Johnny stood up. "There was one more
thing. I brought it back to you. Dave always flew with it—up till the last and afterwards I kept it—with me."

From the side pocket of his tunic she saw
him draw the toy that David's baby hands
had played with—the little broken-eared
rabbit. Then he turned swiftly and went
because he could no longer speak.

Mrs. Armstrong's head, held so calmly
erect during the interview, came slowly forward into her hands as she heard the door
close shut.

Johnny went home, went swiftly to his room and locked himself in. It was growing dusk when he came out, he had taken off his uniform and was dressed in a blue serge suit he had worn before he left. He was composed now.

He went down into the back yard where he had stood two years ago and he called to Mary as he had called two years ago.

There was no answer and no one came to the door.

He crossed over and ran up the steps.

"Mary! Mary-Louise!"

The door was open and Johnny went inside. He had had the run of the house since childhood, so there was little formality about it.

"Mary! Mary!"

Was there no one inside? He ran up the wide stairs that led to the second floor. Maybe they were out on the porch balcony.

At the top of the stairs he stopped short, for something arrested his eye. It was a picture of himself standing on the dresser in Mary's bedroom.

"Mary!"

He trespassed further and looked in.

The room was a shrine. A shrine to himself. It contained every little souvenir of his long companionship with Mary Preston. It was the history of her love. Scattered about the room were a dozen snapshots of himself, taken at various times throughout high-school and college. There were old dance programs, with colored cards and pencils; there were the old school magazines, and scores of clippings from the newspapers as she had followed his air victories. There was the burnt wood box he had given her, and the place cards from the Hallowe'en dinner and the ribbons they'd won at the Senior picnic for the three-legged race.

They were all there, the simple little symbols of a long and loyal companionship. Dear, devoted little Mary. A flood of recollection engulfed him. He understood what he meant to Mary-Louise and he knew what she meant to him.

Where was she? Where could she have gone?

He left the house and crossed over to his own yard. Darkness had come down and the street lamps were lighting up.

At the side of the garage stood the *Shooting Star*. The brave yellow paint on the bonnet had flaked off, and the grass had grown up around the wheels. Mrs. Powell had ousted it from the garage when Johnny went away and it had stood in the yard, forlorn and untouched since.

In the dusk he made out a figure in the seat. Mary-Louise, suffering her final hurt, had crept back to the scene of her first happiness.

"Mary!"

"Hello, Johnny. Welcome home." She made as if to get out of the car.

"Oh, don't go, please. I've been looking for you."

"Have you, Johnny?" She was cool and remote and for the first time since Johnny had known her, he felt humble in her presence.

It occurred to him that she might have

seen him going off with Sylvia and he hastened to explain.

"I wanted—I had to see Sylvia first——"

"Oh, that's all right, Johnny," she said dispassionately, "you needn't explain. I understand."

"But you don't, Mary. You don't really. I want to tell you about it. I had to see Sylvia first to give her Dave's wings. Dave left them with me. She was his sweetheart. They were going to get married when—when he came home."

"Poor Sylvia. . . ."

"And I had to take some things to Mrs. Armstrong. Some of Dave's things."

"Of *course,* Johnny. I understand——"

"Otherwise I would have come straight to you."

"But why do you excuse yourself? I don't mind a bit."

"You don't care?"

"Oh, maybe, for a minute. But it doesn't seem to—to hurt any more."

"Don't you care any more, Mary? At all?"

"Oh, Johnny, what could poor little me mean to you! You with all your fame and great deeds and everything. What could I count for in your life."

"I wish you could understand about me now, Mary," said Johnny painfully. "The reception and all the congratulations and everything just hurt me. I could hardly bear to go through with it. You don't know what happened, do you?"

"About what?"

"About David. How he died."

"We only heard over here that he'd been shot down."

"Well, a terrible thing happened. About the most terrible thing that could have happened to anybody. Nobody knows about it except a few fliers at the field and the Armstrongs. And I'm going to tell you, Mary."

"Don't if it hurts you, Johnny."

He climbed into the seat beside her.

"You see, we were sort of buddies. We didn't like each other much when we went away. You remember? On account of Sylvia, I guess. But afterwards we were thrown together a lot and I found out how fine he was.

"We went through training together and overseas together and we were in the same squadron. We used to fly together. Well, the last time we flew off Dave knew he wasn't coming back. He told me so. You know," said Johnny hesitantly, "there are some things you never can forgive yourself for. I was sore at Dave that day and I wouldn't even wave to him when we took off.

"I thought he was—well—yellow when he told me about his going to be killed. *Yellow*. Why, do you know what Dave did? He tackled a whole Hun squadron single-handed just to protect me. They shot him down and when he landed he shot it out with them on the ground. They took him and sent him back to a prison camp. On the way he dived out of the train window into a tunnel and escaped. Yellow? Do you know what he did after that? He stole a plane from a German flying field and tried to fly it back inside our lines."

"Imagine. Did he succeed?"[1]

"It was the fourth day of the St. Mihiel Drive. I was in the air when he came over. I saw the black crosses on the wings and I thought it was another Hun."

"And you attacked him?"

He nodded dumbly. "After all he'd done, after all his courage and nerve and everything, why, I had to be the one. . . ."

Unconsciously Mary slipped her arm across his bent shoulders. "You mustn't think about it any more."

"I wasn't much good after that," he confessed. "I never brought down another ship. I was glad when it was all over and I could come home."

"Well you're home now, Johnny."

"Can you understand now, Mary, why I don't want to think about the war anymore. I want to forget all about it. I want to stay right here and try to get hold of myself. It's not going to be so easy."

"There is a charm in everyday living," she said.

"Do you know, Mary, all I could think of

on the way home was you. I was coming home to you."

"Why, Johnny! It's Sylvia you care for, isn't it?"

"No, Mary, it's you."

"But, Johnny, you never paid any attention to me. You never cared about me, really."

"I did all the time, but I never knew it. I never knew it until—until I got into trouble and I wanted someone to go to. You see the war was just a kind of a wonderful adventure for me at first. A holiday from school. I didn't care much what happened just so I could fly and get to France and get a crack at the Huns. It was just adventure —until it hurt me, like it hurt everybody else, I guess. That's when I knew I needed you. That's when you find out really who you care for."

"It's very sweet of you to say that, Johnny."

"I've been pretty much all wrong, Mary, since the beginning. I always wanted my own way, and I didn't care much what happened to anybody else so long as I got it. I 'spose you can only go your own way so far, so long, and then life trips you up.''

Mary-Louise regarded him in tender surprise. ''You've no idea how you've changed,'' she said.

''Am I so different?''

''Why, Johnny, you're not the same person at all. I've never heard you talk this way before. In fact I've never really heard you talk about anything before, seriously.''

''Well, I've had a lot of time to think, lately. And I'm only just beginning to understand about things. The things that count, like, oh, like loyalty and friendship and love. The rest doesn't matter much, the glory and all that. No one ever had a finer friend than Dave. I didn't appreciate it; I never even understood the meaning of it until too late.''

''But you were so young, Johnny.''

''You see I can look back now and see how it might have been. If I hadn't been

so thoughtless, if I hadn't done this, if I hadn't taken the locket away from Sylvia
——"

"The locket?"

"Yes, Sylvia had a miniature case with her picture in it that she intended for Dave when he went away. I took it because I thought she meant it for me."

Mary was thinking back to Paris and the night in the Madelon.

"And when I found out about it I was furious with Dave because I thought he had made a fool out of me. The whole thing was that I was just making a fool out of myself," he said bitterly.

"Don't say *that*, Johnny."

"Well, you see, *if* I hadn't hated him that day we went after the balloons, if I had watched for his signals, if I had been there to help him in the fight—why perhaps he'd be here now. You see it all goes back to the very beginning and what was wrong with me."

"But you couldn't know."

"I know now and I'm not going to make, I'm going to try not to make any more mistakes about myself, if I can help it. One thing I have found out, Mary, is that I love you and I always have loved you and I always will love you. You're more important to me than anybody else in the whole world." He groped for her hand in the darkness.

"Why, *Johnny*. . . ."

"All the way back on the boat I was panicky; I was afraid that I'd lost you, that you wouldn't be here when I got back, that you might have met somebody else. There isn't anyone else, is there, Mary?"

She shook her head.

"Gosh, but you're lovely," he said looking at her profile, pale and luminous in the darkness. "I never realized before how beautiful you were."

Mary turned away. "It seems so funny to hear you saying those things to me," she murmured, "and so sweet."

The stars had come out. Lights shone in the windows.

"I love you, Mary, I love you, I love you."

"Do you, blessed?" Her voice was soft and wondering.

"Can you—do you—love me?"

"Don't you know?"

For a time he was silent, staring into the darkness ahead.

"There is something I've got to tell you, Mary. And it's going to be hard. . . ."

"Please don't then."

"I've got to. I'll never feel right about it unless I do. You see, I wanted to come to you as you are coming to me. And I'm afraid I can't. I let myself go once. One night in Paris. . . ." Then he told her the whole sorry tale. About the Folies and the silk stocking in his room in the morning. He left nothing out, he excused himself not at all.

As Mary listened, her eyes lighted up and a mischievous smile played about her lips. Should she tell him? It made her terribly, unspeakably happy to have Johnny make this confession. If he would tell her about this, surely there could have been no other experience in his life.

"It all seems like a dream now," he was saying, "as if it never happened. I don't know who it was. I never want to know. But I didn't think it was fair not to tell you."

"Aren't you ashamed?" said Mary from the far side of the car.

"Yes," he said slowly. "I am ashamed."

Mary forgave him but she never told him. It was to be her secret.

They sat in the car and the darkness increased and they drew closer and closer together. The sound of their voices became less distinct.

Above them a shooting star flashed across the night sky.

"Did you see that?" Johnny asked.

"Of course."

"Well, do you know what the saying is about a shooting star?"

"No," said Mary innocently. "What is it?"

"Well," said Johnny, "well, they say that when you see a shooting star you can kiss the girl you love."

Her face was upturned to his, her lips half open, like a flower.

The whir of wings grew faint and far away in his ears. It grew dim and indistinct and finally died out altogether.

THE END